Pharmacology of the
Carotid Body Chemoreceptors

S. V. ANICHKOV AND M. L. BELEN'KII

Pharmacology of the
Carotid Body Chemoreceptors

TRANSLATED FROM THE RUSSIAN
BY
DR. R. CRAWFORD

A Pergamon Press Book

THE MACMILLAN COMPANY
NEW YORK
1963

THE MACMILLAN COMPANY
60 Fifth Avenue
New York 11, N.Y.

This book is distributed by
THE MACMILLAN COMPANY
pursuant to a special arrangement with
PERGAMON PRESS LIMITED
Oxford, England

Library of Congress Catalog Card Number 63-21068

A translation of the original work
Farmakologiya khimioretseptorov karotidnogo klubochka
Medgiz, Leningrad (1962)

Set in Imprint 11 on 12 pt by Santype Ltd, Salisbury, Wilts and printed
in Great Britain by A. Wheaton & Co. Ltd, Exeter, Devon

1237754

Contents

v

Preface

THIS book is an attempt to present a coherent picture of the
pharmacology of the carotid chemoreceptors based on the results
of a large number of investigations. Our main attention has
naturally been centred on analysis of the researches carried out in
the laboratories directed by one of the authors (S.V.A.). It was
impossible to confine ourselves strictly to the orderly presentation
of accumulated experimental material. Analysis of the selective
action of substances on carotid chemoreceptors offered a possible
line of approach both to discovering the essential nature of the
primary pharmacological reactions occurring in these chemoreceptors and to an understanding of the biochemical basis of chemoreception.

The authors consider it essential to discuss the various concepts
on the mechanism of chemoreception in the carotid body which
have been developed in this country as a result of research on the
pharmacology of this chemoreceptor organ. These concepts have
explained the physiological significance of the reflex reactions
which develop as a result of excitation of the carotid chemoreceptors and have afforded indications for rational lines of research on
still unexplained reflex effects from the carotid bodies. The results
of this research, which are reflected in this book, confirmed that
we were on the right road.

While extension of our knowledge of the reflex effect produced
by excitation of the carotid chemoreceptors is of physiological
interest, it is also of great importance for a fuller understanding
of the effects of therapeutic substances and toxic agents acting on
the chemoreceptors in the carotid bodies. The authors, therefore,
hope that their book will be read not only by physiologists,
pharmacologists, biochemists and pathophysiologists, but also by
clinicians and public health specialists.

S. V. ANICHKOV
M. L. BELEN'KII

Introduction

IN 1894 Pavlov delivered an address entitled "Deficiencies in the current physiological analysis of the action of therapeutic substances" at the 5th Congress of the Society of Russian Doctors, dedicated to the memory of N. I. Pirogov, in which he said: "The comparatively slight attention, relative to the importance of the subject, given to the effects of different substances on the peripheral endings of centripetal nerves must be regarded as a most serious defect. ... These endings must be regarded as extremely varied structures, specific in the same way as nerve endings in the sense organs, and each adapted to its own particular stimulus, whether mechanical, physical or chemical".*

The presence in the tissues of special types of nervous apparatus with specific sensitivity for chemical stimuli, in other words, of chemoreceptors, was thus predicted by Pavlov long before their discovery. Experimental proof of Pavlov's prediction only came some 30 years later.

In 1926 J. Heymans and C. Heymans published the results of experiments that gave convincing proof of the presence of chemoreceptors in the region of the aortic arch, and 4 years later C. Heymans (son) and his co-workers discovered chemoreceptors of extremely high sensitivity in the region of the carotid sinus.

It was then shown that the chemical sensitivity of the carotid sinus region was due to special structures, the carotid bodies, and that Zuckerkandl's bodies, similar in structure to the carotid bodies, were responsible for the chemical sensitivity in the aortic zone.

Even today many physiologists and pathophysiologists give much more attention to baroreceptor reflexes controlling the physical side of circulation than to reflexes from chemoreceptors. Yet the latter obviously play an important part in the control of the chemical properties of the internal environment and the tissues and must, therefore, be of no less importance than reflexes from

* I. P. PAVLOV, Complete Works, vol. 1, p. 525, 1951.

baroreceptors. Contemporary functional biochemistry is probing ever more extensively and profoundly into the fundamental biochemical processes going on in the body. And the physiological importance of chemoreceptors, which regulate these processes and maintain chemical homeostasis in the body, is becoming increasingly evident.

Reactions arising from chemoreceptors are extremely important in pharmacology. The effects of therapeutic substances and poisons after absorption must extend to some degree to proprio-receptors with chemical sensitivity. The reflexes from these receptors play an important part in the development of the effects produced by pharmacological agents.

It has been established (Zakusov, 1938, 1939; Chernigovskii, 1943, 1947, 1960) that the carotid bodies are not by any means the only structures in the body that act as chemoreceptors. Yet, there is no doubt that those of the carotid sinuses have exceptionally high chemical sensitivity and constitute very favourable material for the study of chemoreception.

Our first task was a systematic study of the effects of substances from different pharmacological groups on the chemoreceptors. In view of the large number of experiments which would be necessary for the examination of different substances we decided to use for our experiments animals which would be more convenient than the dogs on which C. Heymans carried out his experiments on the carotid sinus. We therefore selected the cat as our main experimental animal for acute experiments. As our objectives were primarily pharmacological, we sought to avoid in our acute experiments the use of continuous anaesthesia, which would inevitably have produced combined effects of the substance under investigation along with the narcotic agent. Our acute experiments were therefore carried out on decerebrate cats. Isolation of the carotid sinus is the principal method used for analysis of the effects of pharmacological substances on the carotid bodies.

This method was first described and used by Moiseyev (1926) when he was working in N. N. Anichkov's laboratory. Moiseyev used the isolated sinus of the dog in the form of a closed bag filled with Ringer–Locke solution and with its nerve supply intact. He discovered respiratory reflexes from carotid baroreceptors by this method. Moiseyev's method was modified by Heymans for perfusion of the isolated sinus of the dog. We have used the same method, with suitable modifications, in our experiments involving perfusion of the isolated sinus in the cat.

The method used for perfusion of the isolated sinus in the decerebrate cat is as follows. One of the common carotid arteries is exposed in the region of its bifurcation and carefully dissected out. Its branches (internal carotid, occipital, lingual artery, etc.) with the exception of the external carotid are carefully tied in such a way that neither the blood supply nor the innervation of the carotid body (Hering's nerve) are interfered with. The cannula for the introduction of Ringer–Locke solution into the sinus is inserted into the common carotid artery distal to the orifice of the thyroid artery; the outflow cannula is inserted into the external carotid distal to the orifice of the lingual artery. The composition of the fluid used is: NaCl 9·0 g, NaHCO$_3$ 0·2 g, KCl 0·2 g, CaCl$_2$ 0·2 g, glucose 1·0 g in 1 l. of distilled water. From a Mariotte vessel, placed at a height of 1 m, the fluid enters a burette, where it is saturated with oxygen, and it is then heated by passing through a coil in a water bath (Fig. 1). Fluid containing the substance to be tested is supplied from another Mariotte vessel by an exactly similar arrangement. The rate of perfusion (2–3 ml/min) is controlled by a screw clamp on the rubber tubing at the outflow.

In some instances it is desirable, for the study of the sensitivity of the carotid chemoreceptors, to render the perfused isolated sinus completely free from any possible extraneous influences. This is achieved by a method of perfusion of the isolated cat sinus outside the body, developed in our laboratory by Krylov (1956) and used for particularly exact analysis of carotid chemoreceptor sensitivity (Fig. 2).

An examination of various pharmacological agents led us to distinguish two groups of poisons having the most pronounced selective effects on chemoreceptors.

The first group comprises the anoxic poisons (cyanides, sulphides, azides), which block respiratory haemic enzyme systems. The second group consists of the ganglionic poisons, or cholinomimetic substances with actions like that of nicotine. Substances, which excite N-cholinoreactive systems, include nicotine, lobeline, anabasine, cytisine and some others, in addition to acetylcholine and its closest derivatives (Anichkov, 1952). The action on carotid

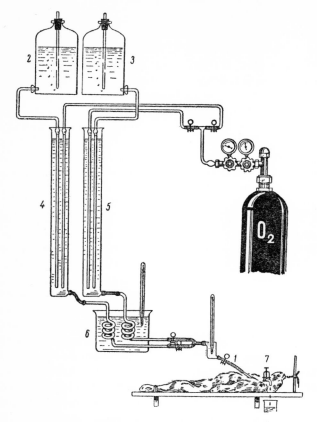

FIG. 1. Arrangement for perfusion of the isolated carotid sinus
in the cat.
1—cannula bringing Ringer–Locke fluid to the sinus. 2, 3—
Mariotte bottles. 4, 5—burettes. 6—vessel containing water.
7—screw clamp on rubber tubing carrying the outlet cannula.

chemoreceptors of poisons in the first group is, apart from its
great theoretical interest, mainly of toxicological importance, but
the selective action of the substances in the second group suggests
the possible use of some of them as therapeutic agents to stimulate
respiration reflexly.

We naturally encountered physiological problems in the course
of our systematic examination of the action of pharmacological

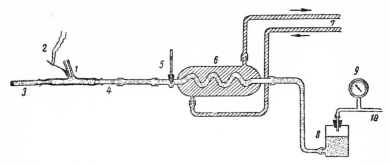

FIG. 2. Diagram of the arrangement for perfusion of the isolated carotid sinus of the cat outside the body
(after Krylov, 1956).
1—isolated preparation of the sinus reflexogenic zone. 2—sinus
nerve on electrodes. 3—outlet cannula. 4—inlet cannula.
5—thermometer. 6—vessel containing a coil for heating the
perfusion fluid. 7—to incubator. 8—vessel containing Ringer–
Locke solution. 9—manometer. 10—to compressor.

agents on the carotid chemoreceptors. There was the inevitable
question of the nature of the chemical sensitivity of proprio-
receptors, or in other words, the biochemical basis of the processes
associated with chemoreceptor excitation resulting from the action
of both physiological and pharmacological stimuli.

Foreign authors have put forward various theories to explain
the development of excitation in the carotid bodies. These
hypotheses and the experimental evidence on which they are based
are discussed and examined in the corresponding chapter.

Belen'kii has made a systematic study of the nature of chemical
sensitivity in the carotid bodies (see Part III). His results led him
to express the view that the immediate cause of excitation in the
carotid bodies in anoxaemia, produced by anoxic poisons and
possibly also by other agents, is disturbance of the energy balance
in the tissue, or more exactly, excess of breakdown over resynthesis of energy-rich bonds. Viewed from this standpoint, the
physiological role of the carotid chemoreceptors is to signal
unfavourable shifts in tissue metabolism leading to disturbance
of the energy balance in the tissues.

We therefore began to re-examine reflexes produced by excitation of carotid chemoreceptors in the light of this concept. With

the exception of the respiratory stimulation and the redistribution of blood, no particular physiological significance is usually attributed to most of these reflexes. The reflex stimulation of respiration in response to deficient oxygen tension in the blood is obviously of compensatory nature and must be regarded as a physiological regulating reaction directed to restoring the level of oxygen tension in the blood. The increase of blood pressure and the reflex redistribution of blood observed on excitation of carotid chemoreceptors is also obviously a compensatory reaction ensuring a better supply of oxygen to the brain in hypoxia.

Other reflexes associated with chemoreceptor excitation have, however, attracted but little attention and no serious attempts have been made to demonstrate their general purpose and physiological significance. Yet, if the chemoreceptors signal disturbances of the energy balance in the tissues, the various associated reflexes must be directed to its restoration, to increase of energy reserves and restriction of their expenditure.

The concept of reflexes from carotid chemoreceptors as compensatory reactions, directed ultimately to the control of biochemical processes in the tissues, led us to make a more extensive examination of these reflexes so that we might be able to give them a physiological meaning. We were unable in these investigations to limit ourselves to the acute mutilating experiments suitable for the analysis of the chemical sensitivity of receptors; it was essential that the animals used in the experiments should have anatomically and functionally intact nervous systems. A special method was, therefore, elaborated in which dogs were submitted to an operation the basis of which was dissection of the sinus by Moiseyev's method as used by Heymans et al. (1932) in their acute experiments. The following method made it possible to bring poisons to act on the dog's carotid chemoreceptors without anaesthesia and to observe the reflexes which developed (Fig. 3).

The operation is carried out under aseptic conditions. The dog is anaesthetized and all branches of the common carotid artery in the region of the sinus, except the lingual artery and the arterioles supplying the glomus, are tied. The common carotid artery is brought out into a skin flap. The wound is sutured and, when it has healed, the dog is ready for experiments. The test substances are injected by syringe into the artery in the skin flap. Once it has become accustomed to the injections, the dog stands quietly in the stand. The substance injected into the common carotid artery only reaches the carotid body and the tongue muscle. When poisons are injected, which are rapidly destroyed in the blood, they do not reach the centres and the reflexes seen are mainly the result of an action on the carotid bodies. Control experiments could thus be carried out on the same dog: the operation was

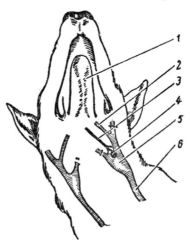

FIG. 3. Diagram of the isolated carotid sinus in the dog in chronic experiment.
1—tongue. 2—lingual artery. 3—sinus nerve. 4—carotid body.
5—carotid sinus. 6—common carotid artery.

performed on both carotid arteries but the nerve supply to the sinus was left intact on one side and Hering's nerve was divided on the other. Effects seen only when a poison was injected into the carotid artery on the side on which the nerve supply to the sinus was intact are obviously the result of reflexes from carotid receptors.

The results, which are described in the succeeding chapters, indicate that reflexes from carotid chemoreceptors embrace a wide range of processes connected with energy metabolism.

PART I

A Brief Account of the Anatomy and Physiology of the Carotid Bodies

THE CAROTID body (glomus caroticum) is situated at the bifurcation of the common carotid artery and is connected with the arterial wall by loose connective tissue. According to the description given by Smirnov (1945), the carotid body in man is usually situated on the medial aspect of the bifurcation. Sometimes, however, it lies on the posteromedial surface of the origin of the external carotid artery, or on the medial aspect of the origin of the occipital artery, or again at the base of the pharyngeal artery. In the cat and dog, the animals most frequently used for experimental study, the carotid body is situated, according to Smirnov's findings, on the medial aspect of the origin of the occipital artery.

The innervation of the carotid body is mainly an afferent one, the nerve being the sinus branch of the glossopharyngeal nerve (Hering's nerve). On the basis of a cytolological examination of the carotid body with the electron microscope, Ross (1959) has expressed the view that the carotid body also has a fairly rich efferent supply.

The carotid body is a very highly vascularized structure. Its blood supply is usually from the artery on which it is situated. Two arterial branches enter the carotid body in the cat and three or four in the dog. The venous outflow drains into the internal jugular vein (Chungcharoen, 1952; Chungcharoen et al., 1952a, 1952b). The arterial branches entering the carotid body divide up into a number of small branches each of which supplies blood to a separate lobe of the glomus and forms therein a dense network of wide capillaries, usually described as blood sinusoids. The nature of the blood supply to the carotid led De Castro (1926, 1927–1928, 1951) to regard the glomeruli of the carotid body as structures consisting of capillaries arranged in arches surrounded by specific cells. The blood from the capillary network of the carotid body is collected in venules which enter an extensive venous plexus in the cellular tissue surrounding the glomus. The venous blood from this plexus enters the internal jugular vein.

An interesting feature of the circulation in the carotid bodies is the system of anastomoses between the arterioles bringing the blood to the capillary network and the venules leaving it. These anastomoses were described by Goormaghtigh and Pannier (1939). Their existence has been confirmed by De Boissezon (1943, 1944), De Castro (1940) and Celestino da Costa (1944). De Castro (1951) made a detailed study of these anastomoses and found that they were equipped with powerful muscle cells situated under the endothelium. Contraction of these cells closes the lumina of the anastomoses with resultant increased filling of the glomus and slowing of the venous outflow. Conversely, when the arterio-venous anastomoses open up, the filling of the glomus with blood is reduced and the rate of outflow into the veins increases. The size of the carotid body thus depends on the state of the arterio-venous anastomoses and it may change by one-fifth or one-sixth of its average volume in either direction.

Daly *et al.* (1954) measured the minute-volume of blood flow in the carotid body by some very delicate experiments on cats. The volume of flow was found to depend directly on the level of arterial pressure. The rate of flow in the carotid body rose considerably when adrenaline was injected into the animal, fell when the arterial pressure fell and actually reached zero when the arterial pressure fell to 40–50 mm Hg. Results obtained in experiments on six cats, in which the average blood pressure was 130 mm Hg, revealed that an average of 38 μl of blood flowed through the carotid body in the course of 1 min. If, as is usually done, the flow is calculated per 100 g of tissue, the volume rate of flow through the glomus is found to be 200 ml/100 g per min. The carotid body has thus a richer blood supply than any other organ. The minute-volume per 100 g of tissue is 60 ml in the brain, 64–151 ml in heart muscle (left ventricle) and 560 ml in the thyroid gland.

Ross (1959) gives a detailed description of the microscopic structure of the carotid body, and he describes the carotid body in the cat as a structure surrounded by a dense fibrous tissue capsule, consisting of islets of chemoreceptor cells separated from one another by blood sinusoids and surrounded by a plexus of nerve fibres.

Occasional ganglion cells, unconnected with the specific cells, are seen in the peripheral part of the carotid body. These would appear to have some connexion with the vascular nerve supply.

Bundles of medullated nerve fibres are also seen at the periphery of the glomus (Boyd, 1937a, 1937b; Smirnov, 1945; Hollinshead and Sawyer, 1945; De Kock, 1951, 1954; Ross, 1959; and others).

Using the electron microscope, Lever and Boyd (1957), Hoffman and Birrell (1958) and Garner and Duncan (1958) have obtained evidence of the existence in the glomeruli of two types of cell showing different degrees of electron beam penetration. A detailed electron microscope examination of the carotid body of the cat has been carried out by Ross (1959).

Ross has also distinguished two types of cell in the carotid body with the ordinary light microscope. The most numerous are polygonal cells with rounded nuclei, which are apparently the chemoreceptor cells. The cells of the other type have dense ellipsoid nuclei, with long processes leaving the cell body and coming into close connexion with the chemoreceptor cells. Ordinary microscopic examination affords evidence that nerve fibres are intimately connected with both types of cell. By the help of the electron microscope, Ross was able to add considerable detail and to extend our conceptions of the fine morphological relationships existing in the carotid body.

These observations by Ross indicate that there is only one type of chemoreceptor cell in the carotid body and that these cells are in direct synaptic connexion with fibres from the system of the glossopharyngeal nerve; Ross failed to observe any signs of the existence of intermediate synapses, as postulated by Meijling (1938) and De Kock (1951, 1954).

As in other synapses, there is a synaptic cleft between chemo-receptor cell and nerve fibre. As was noted by Ross (1959), however, this synapse differs in certain respects from synapses in efferent systems: there is no pronounced thickening of the presynaptic and postsynaptic membranes, there is no concentration of mitochondria in the region of synaptic contact within the presynaptic structure (chemoreceptor cell), and minute vesicles, similar in size to "synaptic vesicles", are scattered throughout the entire cytoplasm of the chemoreceptor cells and are not concentrated in the synaptic region. Ross is of the opinion that these features may be connected with the fact that the nerve fibre enters into synaptic contact with the chemoreceptor cell at several points, and not merely one point, on its surface. Ross also notes that the synapses between receptor cells and afferent nerve fibres in other receptor structures do not present the morphological features peculiar to synapses in efferent systems.

Early investigations on chemoreceptors in the carotid sinus zone (Heymans and Bouckaert, 1930; Heymans *et al.*, 1930) had already established that chemoreceptors react by excitation to reduced oxygen tension, to increased partial pressure of carbon dioxide and to increase of hydrogen ion concentration in the arterial blood bathing the carotid sinus region. The importance of chemoreceptors was clearly evident in the hypoxia produced by reduction of the oxygen content of the inspired air, which is followed by a reduction of the oxygen tension in the arterial blood. In this form of hypoxic hypoxia there occurs violent panting and a rise of blood pressure. Numerous investigations testify that these phenomena are fully accounted for by reflexes from carotid body chemoreceptors.

Carotid body chemoreceptors are regarded as playing a particularly important part in the hypoxic hypoxia which is dependent on primary depression of the respiratory centre in the narcosis produced by barbiturates or bromethol (Avertin; Narkolan) and also in morphine poisoning. There is experimental evidence that the inhalation of carbon dioxide does not increase pulmonary ventilation and the breathing of oxygen precipitates profound depression or even arrest of respiratory movement in states of profound narcosis produced by these substances and after the injection of large doses of morphine (Mulinos and Atheneos, 1932; Marshall and Rosenfeld, 1935, 1936; Comroe and Schmidt, 1938; Marri and Rindi, 1940; Dripps and Dunke, 1943; and others).

On such evidence the theory was advanced that barbiturates, avertin and morphine pre-eminently suppressed the excitability of the respiratory centre in response to humoral stimuli, including carbon dioxide. This implies that the reflex excitability of the respiratory centre remains intact. The result would be that the control of respiration would be readjusted from humoral to reflex and that reflexes from chemoreceptors would become the main factor in maintaining the activity of the respiratory centre.

It is hardly possible to agree that profound barbiturate narcosis leads to a change in the nature of respiratory regulation. It is more logical to think that it would be more difficult to compensate for the loss of chemoreceptor impulses from the carotid bodies in narcotized animals than in intact or even in decerebrate animals.

In Belen'kii's experiments (1951) denervation of the carotid sinus regions (by infiltration with 1% procaine solution) in cats in a state of profound thiopental narcosis led to the development of periodic respiration or complete arrest of respiratory movements in 5 out of 10 instances. At the same time, in decerebrate cats, severe disturbances of respiration as a result of the infiltration of the carotid sinus zones with procaine were observed in only one out of twelve experiments. Respiratory depression produced by loss of the chemoreceptor reflexes could, however, be abolished by the intravenous injection of leptazol, which is a typical analeptic with direct central action, in cats narcotized with thiopental. This would indicate that, in profound thiopental narcosis, the respiratory centre still retains its excitability by agents which stimulate it directly. Booker *et al.* (1950) have also found that the respiratory depression produced by thiopental could be abolished by appropriate doses of leptazol. Kudrin (1950) found that leptazol was also an effective analeptic in the narcosis produced by other barbiturates such as hexobarbitone.

A question of considerable importance in connexion with the development of concepts on the function of the carotid bodies is their role in anaemic hypoxias, the forms of oxygen deficiency due to reduction in the oxygen-carrying power of the blood.

Carbon monoxide poisoning is probably the form of anaemic hypoxia which has been most studied. Most investigators have noted that this form of hypoxia is not associated with the development of reflexes from the carotid body chemoreceptors even when the carboxyhaemoglobin content of the blood is high. Most have in fact found that there is no reflex stimulation of respiration in carbon monoxide poisoning (Comroe and Schmidt, 1938; Ardashnikova and Shik, 1948; Chiodi *et al.*, 1941; Lilienthal, 1950; Duke *et al.*, 1953).

As a result of their investigations these authors came to the conclusion that if respiratory acceleration did occur when CO was breathed, it was of central origin and depended on acidosis.

Working in our laboratory, M. A. Grebenkina reached a different conclusion. Making her observations on decerebrate cats inhaling high carbon monoxide concentrations, she noted that panting was much less evident in the animals with the carotid sinuses denervated. Obviously reflexes from the carotid bodies played some part in the respiratory stimulation associated with rapid rise in the carbon monoxide content of the blood. When carbon monoxide poisoning, even to a severe degree, developed slowly, the carotid bodies did not play an important part in the intoxication. This seems also to be true in hypoxia produced by substances causing methaemoglobin formation (see Dripps and Comroe, 1944).

The absence of any signs of excitation of the carotid body chemoreceptors in the anaemic form of hypoxia led to the conclusion that the chemoreceptors reacted exclusively to reduction of oxygen tension in the blood, as determined by the quantity of oxygen dissolved in the plasma (Comroe and Schmidt, 1938; Dripps and Comroe, 1944; Ardashnikova, 1947; Marshak, 1948; Kulik, 1947; Ardashnikova and Shik, 1949; Wyss, 1949; Duke et al., 1953; and others).

On this basis Comroe and Schmidt (1938) arrived at the erroneous conclusion that the tissues of the carotid body had a low oxygen consumption. They considered that the oxygen consumption of the carotid body tissues was so small that it could be completely satisfied by the oxygen dissolved in the blood plasma (0·3 ml/100 ml).

The error of Comroe and Schmidt became obvious when Daly et al. (1954) carried out their delicate experiments for direct determination of the oxygen consumption of the carotid body tissue in the cat. It was shown that, when the volume rate of blood flow was maintained at a level of 10 μl/min, the arterial–venous difference in oxygen was 2 ml/100 ml. If it is assumed that all the blood reaching the glomus passes through its tissue and that the average weight of the carotid body is 2 g, then the oxygen consumption of the carotid body tissue is 9 ml/min per 100 g tissue. This value is evidence of an exceptionally high oxygen consumption in the carotid body, i.e. three times the oxygen consumption of brain tissue (Kety and Schmidt, 1945). Actually, the oxygen consumption of the carotid body tissues is probably even higher still as it can reasonably be assumed that some of the blood does not pass through the glomus but enters the veins through the arteriovenous anastomoses.

Daly *et al.* (1954) adduce the high rate of blood flow to explain why, despite their large oxygen requirement, the carotid bodies are satisfied with the quantity of oxygen dissolved in the blood plasma. These investigators have shown that 2000 ml of blood per 100 g tissue per minute flow through the carotid body. With this very profuse blood supply the carotid body must be able to obtain its large oxygen requirement solely from the oxygen dissolved in the plasma. Daly *et al.* base this conclusion on fairly convincing calculations. It may be noted that Shik (1949) expressed exactly the same view on the method whereby the carotid body tissues obtained their oxygen, long before the investigations of Daly and others.

It may be mentioned here that reduction of the volume rate of blood flow through the carotid body in consequence of fall of blood pressure to 50 mm Hg following withdrawal of blood leads to development of signs of chemoreceptor activity (Landgren and Neil, 1951). Referring to Landgren's work, Heymans and Neil (1958) point out that reduction of blood pressure produces excitation of chemoreceptors even when pure oxygen is being breathed.

The sensitivity of the carotid body chemoreceptors to carbon dioxide was demonstrated at the same time as their sensitivity to oxygen deficiency (Heymans and Booker, 1930; Heymans *et al.*, 1930). The stimulating effect of carbon dioxide on carotid chemoreceptors was subsequently confirmed by many investigations (see reviews by Heymans *et al.*, 1933; Heymans and Booker, 1939; Heymans, 1941; Schmidt and Comroe, 1940; Schmidt, 1940; Dripps and Comroe, 1944; Chernigovskii, 1947; Heymans 1955; Heymans and Neil, 1958). The breathing of carbon dioxide produces dyspnoea through its action on the chemoreceptors in the carotid bodies. This dyspnoea persists, however, even after the carotid sinus regions have been denervated. Consequently the fact that hypercapnia, as distinct from hypoxia, can produce respiratory stimulation through the direct action of carbon dioxide on the respiratory centre was never doubted by any investigator.

Detailed analysis of a considerable volume of experimental material on this subject enabled Schmidt and Comroe (1940) to conclude that the role of chemoreceptors in the reaction to hypercapnia only became obvious when the direct sensitivity of the respiratory centre to carbon dioxide was reduced, as when the blood contained large quantities of carbon dioxide and in profound narcosis. Under such conditions respiration can be maintained through reflex stimulation of the respiratory centre by hypercapnic impulses from the carotid chemoreceptors.

Reflexes can be seen to develop from the isolated carotid sinus when the hydrogen ion concentration of the perfusing fluid is increased (Heymans *et al.*, 1930; see also reviews by Heymans *et al.*, 1933; Gesell, 1939, Schmidt and Comroe, 1940; Dripps and Comroe, 1944; Chernigovskii, 1947; Heymans and Neil, 1958; and others). Winterstein (1953, 1956) suggested that even carbon dioxide acts on chemoreceptors as an agent increasing hydrogen ion concentration.

All investigators are agreed that, when there is severe hypercapnia and severe uncompensated acidosis, chemoreceptors play a very much greater part in the reactions which develop and may even assume the role of the sole factor maintaining the activity of vital centres.

The American Pharmacological School directed by Schmidt also takes the view that the importance of the carotid body chemoreceptors is restricted in this way and they regard the chemoreceptors as an apparatus which becomes involved in processes for the control of respiration and circulation only when the organism experiences "unusual circumstances" or, in other words, in pathological states (Schmidt, 1940, 1944, 1956; Schmidt and Comroe, 1940; Dripps and Comroe, 1944). This school denies that the carotid chemoreceptors play any part in the control of respiration under ordinary physiological conditions.

The recording of potentials from the sinus nerve has, however, introduced quite substantial evidence that the carotid bodies are constantly involved in the control of respiration.

It has been demonstrated that impulses with discharge frequencies of the order of 20–40/sec are constantly passing along the sinus nerve. As the frequency of the discharges increases in asphyxia, it must be assumed that the source of these impulses is the constant tonic activity of chemoreceptors (Heymans and Rijlant, 1933). Convincing confirmation of the tonic activity of chemoreceptors has been provided by Euler *et al.* (1939), who recorded electrical phenomena in the glossopharyngeal nerve in a preparation containing only chemoreceptor fibres. Constant discharges were observed in the nerve even when the arterial blood was 96% saturated with oxygen; steps were taken to ensure that there was ample pulmonary ventilation in the experimental animal (cat) during the experiment; any possibility that the chemoreceptor activity was of hypercapnic origin was thus completely excluded.

Giving the grounds for his view that carotid body chemoreceptors are an apparatus which has no part in physiological regulations when conditions in the body are normal, Schmidt (1940) stated that the chemoreceptor function of the carotid body is a "vestige of the primitive type of respiratory control required by water-breathing animals". This concept of carotid body chemoreceptors as "ancient" rudimentary apparatuses has been effectively countered by the investigations of Koch (1931) and Boyd (1937a, 1937b) on the ontogenesis of the carotid bodies. These investigators found that the carotid body is formed from the mesoderm of the third branchial arch and that the sinus nerve develops from the nerve supplying this arch. On this evidence Koch concluded that the chemoreceptors in this region must play an important part in the control of respiration in fishes. His opinion was that the central nervous system in fishes obtained information on the oxygen tension in the water bathing the gill system through the chemoreceptor apparatus. The view has also been expressed that fishes are guided in the selection of their particular habitat by the signals received from chemoreceptors on the oxygen tension of the water (Sepp, 1949). In keeping with these views, there is a considerable amount of experimental evidence that fishes are only very slightly sensitive to carbon dioxide and that reduced oxygen tension in the water is of primary importance for respiratory regulation (Babak, 1907; Babak and Dedek, 1907; Olthoff, 1934; Meyer, 1935; Van Dam, 1938; Krogh, 1941; Kravchinskii, 1945; and others), control being effected by reflex mechanisms originating in branchial chemoreceptors. At the same time, we must mention the work of Adrian and Buitendijk (1931) on the isolated nervous system of the goldfish. It was found in this investigation that potentials with a rate similar to that of the gill movement also developed in the isolated central nervous system of the fish, an observation which would indicate that the respiratory centre in the fish could function even in the absence of any afferent nerve stimulation.

If we accept that chemoreceptor apparatuses are vitally important in water-breathing animals and agree with Schmidt's view that in mammals they are merely "vestiges of primitive forms of respiratory regulation", then it must be expected that the sensitivity of chemoreceptor apparatuses would decline progressively from lower to higher animal species. More particularly, it should be expected that the sensitivity of chemoreceptors in amphibians, which is the class nearest to fishes, would be greater, or at any rate not less, than the sensitivity in mammals, as the main factor controlling respiration in amphibians is oxygen lack (Krogh, 1904), a condition which, in mammals, can stimulate respiration only through a reflex from chemoreceptors.

The mechanism of pulmonary respiration in the frog is rather a peculiar one (Babak, 1913, 1921; Karasik, 1930). Respiration is here effected by two types of respiratory movement—oropharyngeal and pulmonary.

In the frog the respiratory reaction to hypoxia runs a very characteristic course (Babak, 1921; Karasik, 1930, 1934, 1948): series of active pulmonary movements develop; each series consists of a number of movements emptying the lungs followed by a number of charging movements which distend the pulmonary sacs. In the intervals between the series oropharyngeal movements may be observed or, should there be a very violent dyspnoeic reaction, there will be no respiratory movements at all. Karasik (1930) has shown that the characteristic picture of dyspnoea develops in the frog immediately after the injection of cyanide which, in mammals, is known to produce a dyspnoea solely dependent on reflexes originating in the chemoreceptors of the carotid body (see next chapter).

In the frog there is in the region of the bifurcation of the common carotid artery a formation of cavernous structure which is formed from the third branchial arch and receives its nerve supply from the glossopharyngeal nerve (Maurer, 1888; Marshall, 1893; Ecker and Wiedershein, 1896; Mayer, 1927; Palme, 1934; Smirnov, 1944, 1945; and others). This structure, which is termed the carotid body (synonyms: carotid labyrinth, vascular labyrinth, carotid gland etc.) is considered to be the homologue of the mammalian carotid body (Ask-Upmark, 1935). Depressor reflexes, similar to the reflexes observed in mammals on increase of blood pressure in the carotid sinus, develop from the region of the carotid body (Nikiforovskii, 1912, 1913; Kuno and Brucke, 1914; Mayer, 1927). The chemoreceptor function in the carotid body of the frog was investigated by Karasik (1934). He found that division of the glossopharyngeal nerves did not prevent development of a dyspnoeic reaction in response to the injection of cyanide. On this evidence Karasik expressed the view that a respiratory reaction to hypoxia can develop in the frog even in the absence of reflexes from the carotid sinus region. Different results were obtained by Smyth (1939). He denervated the carotid bodies in chronic experiments by painting them with phenol; thereafter, he was no longer able to observe a dyspnoeic reaction when the animals were placed in an atmosphere of nitrogen. Smyth points out that the frogs operated on by him were in extremely grave condition and died a few hours after the operation. It is, therefore, hardly possible to conclude that the absence of a respiratory reaction to hypoxia after denervation of the carotid bodies was actually due to exclusion of these bodies.

In 1946 Belen'kii repeated Smyth's experiments, using potassium cyanide (0·025–0·1% solutions prepared with sodium chloride solution so that the final solution was isotonic) as the agent producing hypoxia. The method of excluding the carotid bodies was improved and the painting of the bodies with phenol was replaced by their complete removal together with the adjoining segments of vessels. As a result of this improved technique the frogs survived for from 3 to 8 days after the operation and their behaviour appeared to be quite normal. Potassium cyanide produced dyspnoeic reactions in animals operated on in this manner which were no less pronounced than the reactions in intact animals (Fig. 4).

It must be particularly emphasized that the exclusion of the carotid bodies in these experiments neither influenced the intensity of the dyspnoeic reaction nor raised the threshold of the animals' sensitivity to cyanide. It follows from Belen'kii's experiments that the carotid bodies in the frog, as distinct from those of mammals, take no part in the development of respiratory reactions to cyanide. In other words, chemoreceptor function in the carotid sinus region in an animal close to the fishes is not of the same importance in the development of reactions to hypoxia as it is in mammals, animals which are far ahead of fishes in evolution. Belen'kii found that respiration in the frog was only very slightly sensitive to nicotine, a typical chemoreceptor-stimulating poison. Popov and Egolinskii (1929) have likewise shown that lobeline produces no respiratory reactions in frogs. It should be added

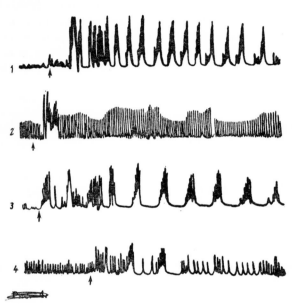

FIG. 4. Frog (male, weight 41 g). Right sacral plexus divided Recording of respiration. The arrows indicate the injection of 0·5 ml 0·025% solution of potassium cyanide (3γ/g) subcutaneously on the right side.
1—before extirpation of the carotid bodies. 2—4 hr 5 min after extirpation. 3—24 hr 40 min after extirpation. 4—68 hr after extirpation (on the day of the animal's death).

that Palme (1934) found that the carotid bodies in the frog contained no cell elements similar to the specific cells in the mammalian carotid body.

It is important to note that both nicotine and lobeline produce respiratory excitation in animals of higher phylogenetic development (reptiles); unlike the corresponding reaction in mammals, however, this reaction persists after denervation of the carotid sinus and aortic zones. The reaction to hypoxia (injection of cyanide or sulphide, breathing of nitrogen) is also retained under these circumstances (Boelaert, 1947).

Generally, therefore, it must be concluded that experimental evidence on the phylogenesis of the chemoreceptor function of the carotid sinus zone is incompatible with the concept of this function as a "vestige of a primitive type of respiratory regulation peculiar to water-breathing animals". On the contrary, the facts indicate that the chemoreceptor function of the carotid body is a manifestation of biological progress, developing in relatively late stages of animal evolution.

It is interesting to compare observations on the ontogenesis of chemoreceptor function in the carotid bodies with what is known of its phylogenesis. Observing the foetus through an opening in the wall of the uterus of the pregnant rabbit, Snyder and Rosenfeld (1936) noted movements of the thorax and anterior abdominal wall with a rate of about 60/min immediately before birth. When the pregnant rabbit was placed in conditions producing oxygen starvation, it developed dyspnoea but the "respiratory" movements in the foetus were slowed. Thus, the foetus still had no power to react by respiratory excitation to oxygen deficiency. According to Volokhov and Obraztsova (1950), hypoxia produces respiratory excitation in young rabbits on the first postnatal day but the reaction becomes more pronounced as age increases.

Working with puppies and young rats, Pal'gova and Volobuyev (1940) have shown that the older the animal, the earlier is the development of respiratory excitation when the oxygen tension in the inspired air is gradually reduced.

Krasnovskaya (1941, 1943) and Rozanova (1947) found that chemoreceptors in puppies only began to function at the age of 16–18 days. Polosukhin (1947) and Lauer (1949) also noted that the chemoreceptor system did not function in newborn animals or was less well-developed than in adult animals.

The fact that chemoreceptors attain full functional maturity some time after birth is likewise inconsistent with the concept of these chemoreceptors as of "ancient" origin and regressive biological significance.

PART II

Effects of Pharmacological Agents on the Chemoreceptors of the Carotid Bodies

CHAPTER I

Poisons Producing Tissue Hypoxia

CYANIDES

The power of cyanide to arrest tissue respiration by blocking cytochrome oxidase activity (Warburg, 1946) is the basis of its pharmacological effect. Hydrocyanic acid and its salts are, therefore, classed as hypoxic poisons, causing tissue or histotoxic hypoxia.

After it was demonstrated by the Heymans School that the tissue of the carotid bodies was not less, but more sensitive to hypoxia than brain tissue and that many apparently central phenomena observed in hypoxia are primarily the result of reflexes arising from carotid chemoreceptors, it was natural to speculate on the possible participation of such reflexes in the picture of poisoning produced by cyanides, particularly in the first "dyspnoeic" period of poisoning. This raised the question as to the effect of cyanide on the carotid bodies.

In the early 'thirties Heymans and his co-workers published investigations proving conclusively that the excitation of the respiratory and other bulbar centres in the first "dyspnoeic" period of hydrocyanic acid poisoning is the result of reflexes from the carotid sinus reflexogenic zone (Heymans *et al.*, 1931a, 1931b, 1931c, 1931d; Heymans *et al.*, 1932).

The carotid receptors are extremely sensitive to cyanide. Experiments by Heymans and his co-workers have shown that the injection of 10γ potassium cyanide into the common carotid artery of the dog produces powerful excitation of the carotid bodies and corresponding reflexes in the bulbar centres.

The extreme sensitivity of the carotid chemoreceptors to cyanide has been confirmed by Winder *et al.* (1939).

Perfusing the isolated sinus, Mel'nikova (1952) made a special study of the sensitivity of the carotid sinuses to cyanide in decerebrate cats. The indicator of carotid body reaction was the change in the cat's respiration. In these experiments reflex respiratory excitation was first observed when the isolated sinus was perfused with potassium cyanide in concentration of 10^{-7}. With a stronger solution (10^{-6}) there was more powerful reflex respiratory excitation and a concentration of 10^{-5} produced violent dyspnoea.

The method of perfusing the isolated sinus was useful not only in establishing the threshold concentration of cyanide to which the chemoreceptors were sensitive, but also made it possible to observe the changes in the sensitivity of the chemoreceptors associated with repeated and prolonged application of cyanide. Potassium cyanide in Ringer's solution was passed through the isolated sinus for periods of from 20 min to 1 hr. When perfusion was carried out for these periods with cyanide concentrations of 10^{-6} and 10^{-5}, there was very violent initial respiratory excitation lasting 40–50 sec, after which respiration gradually quietened down and, despite continuation of the cyanide perfusion, the respiratory rate and excursion regained their initial levels.

The conclusion is that carotid receptors become less sensitive to cyanide as a result of prolonged exposure. This decline of sensitivity was confirmed in Mel'nikova's experiments in which the isolated sinus was repeatedly perfused with cyanide. In these experiments, after the sinus had been perfused for a certain length of time with potassium cyanide solution, it was washed through with pure Ringer–Locke solution and then again perfused with a cyanide solution of the same strength. When washing was carried out for a short time only, exposure to cyanide produced less powerful excitation than the preceding exposure. The degree to which chemoreceptor sensitivity was depressed depended on the cyanide concentration and the duration of the perfusion. Potassium cyanide 10^{-6} merely produced temporary and only relative insensitivity of the carotid chemoreceptors; repeated perfusion with the same concentration produced reactions which were almost the same as the original reaction and recovery was readily brought about by washing. Potassium cyanide 10^{-5} produced complete chemoreceptor insensitivity after prolonged perfusion: repeated cyanide perfusion failed to produce respiratory reactions. This failure was reversible, however, and the original reaction to perfusion with cyanide was restored after washing for from 20 min to 1 hr. Irreversible chemoreceptor paralysis was only produced by prolonged perfusion of the isolated carotid sinus with potassium cyanide 10^{-4}.

Anichkov and Belen'kii (1948) have shown that prolonged action of potassium cyanide on the carotid sinuses abolishes sensitivity not only to cyanide itself but also to substances which, although possessing selective action on carotid chemoreceptors, are not hypoxic poisons. It was found that acetylcholine and nicotine no longer exercised their usual excitatory effect on carotid chemoreceptors after prolonged perfusion of the isolated sinus of decerebrate cats with potassium cyanide in concentrations of 10^{-5} and 2×10^{-5} (Fig. 5). Prolonged cyanide action on the carotid bodies thus led to loss of their sensitivity both to hypoxic poisons and to substances stimulating cholinoreactive systems, substances with quite different action mechanisms.

It must be remembered that the absence of respiratory stimulation when the carotid bodies are acted on by a given substance

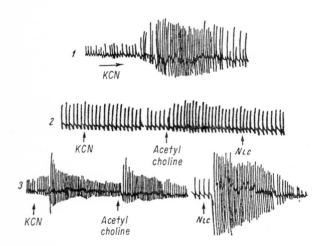

Fig. 5. Decerebrate cat. Perfusion of the isolated carotid sinus. Recording of respiration.
1—commencement of perfusion with potassium cyanide (1/50,000). 2—injection into the perfusing fluid of 0·4 ml of potassium cyanide (1/5000), acetylcholine (1/5000) and nicotine (1/40,000) during continuous cyanide perfusion. 3—injection of the same drugs 10 min after the commencement of flushing with Ringer–Locke solution.

may be due to depression of the reflex excitability of the respiratory centre as a result of its prolonged and intense "bombardment" with impulses from the carotid bodies rather than to loss of chemoreceptor excitability. This possibility was investigated in the work of Anichkov and Belen'kii. It was found that after reflex respiratory reactions from the perfused carotid sinus had been abolished by prolonged exposure to cyanide, the intravenous injection of cyanide continued to produce a violent respiratory reaction, the source of which was, of course, the carotid body of the opposite side.

The electrical activity in the sinus nerve recorded during the action of cyanide on the carotid chemoreceptors provides information of great value for more accurate assessment of the effect of cyanides on the carotid bodies.

A very accurate method for electrophysiological analysis of the effects of pharmacological substances on carotid chemoreceptors is the method developed by Krylov (1956) for perfusion of the isolated sinus outside the body. When this method is used the electrical activity in the sinus nerve is a direct indicator of the effect of the poisons on the carotid chemoreceptors. And the experimental results cannot be influenced either by the state of the centres or the state of the sympathetic ganglia.

Just as in the experiments on the intact animal, very powerful initial excitation of the carotid chemoreceptors and subsequent complete loss of sensitivity were observed when the carotid bodies were exposed to the action of cyanide by perfusion of the completely isolated sinus.

In Krylov's experiments the injection of 0·5 mg sodium cyanide (0·5 ml of 0·1% solution) into the Ringer–Locke solution perfusing the completely isolated sinus produced a sharp increase of the rate and considerable increase in the size of the oscillations recorded electrographically from the sinus nerve. The changes in the oscillations developed about 10 sec after cyanide had been injected, not immediately. Diminishing gradually, the enhanced electrical activity in the nerve lasted for 2 or 3 min. When the injection of cyanide into the stream of fluid was repeated at 2-min intervals, each fresh injection produced progressively weaker excitation of the chemoreceptors. After five or six injections cyanide ceased to have any stimulating effect on the chemoreceptors or on the oscillations.

The same initial increase of electrical activity with subsequent decline was observed when the completely isolated sinus was perfused continuously with adequately strong concentrations of cyanide. When the sinus was perfused with a 1:25,000 solution of sodium cyanide in Ringer–Locke fluid there was a sharp increase in the frequency and amplitude of the oscillations. This continued for 2 or 3 min, after which, although the cyanide perfusion was continued, the electrical activity in the nerve declined and disappeared altogether.

Perfusing the completely isolated sinus, Krylov confirmed the findings of Anichkov and Belen'kii that prolonged action of cyanide abolished the sensitivity of the carotid chemoreceptors not only to cyanide but also to acetylcholine and cholinomimetic substances. In Krylov's experiments five or six injections of 0·5 mg sodium cyanide into the perfusion fluid abolished the reaction of the carotid bodies of the completely isolated sinus not only to the succeeding injection of cyanide but also to acetylcholine, nicotine and cytisine. There was the same loss of sensitivity to acetylcholine and cholinomimetic substances after continuous perfusion of the completely isolated sinus with 1:50,000–1:25,000 solutions of potassium cyanide. It may be noted that prolonged cyanide perfusion led first of all to disappearance of the reaction to the next cyanide perfusion and later, to disappearance of the reactions to acetylcholine and cholinomimetic poisons. When the cyanide perfusion was stopped and the isolated sinus was flushed with pure Ringer–Locke solution for 1 min, chemoreceptor sensitivity to cyanide as well as to acetylcholine, potassium chloride, nicotine and cytisine was completely restored after 10 min.

The main features in the reaction of carotid chemoreceptors to cyanide are thus: intense initial excitation, observed even with quite low concentrations, and subsequent disappearance of sensitivity for both hypoxic poisons and other carotid chemoreceptor stimuli.

The carotid bodies are more sensitive to cyanide than other tissues.

Brain tissue is known to be particularly sensitive to hypoxia and hypoxic poisons. Heymans and his co-workers have shown that the first signs of the action of hydrocyanic acid and cyanide, and particularly the dyspnoea, are due to reflexes from the carotid bodies. The latter are, therefore, more sensitive to cyanide than brain tissue.

The character of the reaction of the carotid bodies to hypoxic poisons is also distinctive. Cyanide, even in high dilution, produces intense chemoreceptor excitation. Chemoreceptor paralysis is only observed after more or less prolonged exposure to concentrations ten times higher. Some centres, particularly the respiratory centre, are depressed by the direct action of cyanide without preliminary excitation (Heymans *et al.*, 1931b).

The rapid loss of consciousness in cyanide poisoning suggests that the higher cortical centres are likewise depressed by cyanide without any important preliminary excitation.

Mel'nikova (1952) made a comparative study of sensitivity to cyanide in the carotid bodies, sympathetic ganglia and the adrenal medulla, structures which react very similarly to some pharmacological substances. There was considerable difference between the sensitivity of the carotid bodies and the sensitivities of the sympathetic ganglia and adrenal medulla. The latter did not manifest anything like the same sensitivity to cyanide as the carotid bodies and they did not react by the excitation characteristic of the latter.

The excessively high sensitivity of the carotid chemoreceptors to cyanide is supported by the finding of exceptionally intense oxidative processes in the tissue of these bodies (Daly *et al.*, 1954).

The great sensitivity of the carotid bodies to cyanide makes it possible to utilize the action of these substances on the carotid sinus as a simple method for studying the reflexes which develop in hypoxic excitation of the carotid chemoreceptors.

This method has been used very extensively for the study of reflexes from the carotid bodies by Soviet pharmacologists.

Respiratory Reflexes

Heymans *et al.* (1931b, 1931d) used several methods, each supplementing the other, in their experiments.

In some experiments a small dose of potassium cyanide (0·2 ml of 0·2% solution) was injected into the common carotid artery of the dog. If the innervation of the carotid sinus was intact, the cyanide injection produced violent respiratory excitation. When the carotid sinus had previously been denervated, the same doses of cyanide produced no respiratory changes whatever. Nor were changes observed when the cyanide solution was injected into the vertebral or internal carotid artery, which meant that the cyanide went directly to the brain without passing through the carotid sinus. Even considerably larger doses given by these routes did not lead to respiratory excitation. Indeed, these larger doses, acting directly on the centres, produced some degree of respiratory depression. These experiments with intra-arterial injections of cyanide showed that the respiratory excitation produced by the hydrocyanic acid ions is solely the result of a reflex from the carotid chemoreceptors. This conclusion was confirmed by further experiments of Heymans *et al.* in which potassium cyanide was injected intravenously. When cyanide was injected intravenously into dogs in which the nerve supplies of the sinuses were intact, powerful respiratory excitation developed, but this did not occur when cyanide was injected into dogs with the carotid sinuses denervated. These results were obtained with both anaesthetized and unanaesthetized dogs. Finally, the decisive proof of the reflex nature of the respiratory excitation produced by cyanide is that such excitation could be produced by very low concentrations of cyanide on the isolated carotid sinus with its nerves intact (Mel'nikova, 1952).

Reflex Changes in Heart Rate

Heymans *et al.* (1931c) have shown that the action of cyanide on carotid chemoreceptors produces reflex excitation of the vagus nerve centres for the heart as well as respiratory reflexes. When a small quantity of potassium cyanide (0·1 mg) was injected into the common carotid artery of the dog, there was slowing of the heart. This slowing did not occur when the same dose of cyanide was injected into the common carotid artery after denervation of its sinus or directly into the vertebral or internal carotid artery beyond the sinus receptors, that is directly into the blood stream going to the brain.

This slowing of the pulse produced by cyanide does not depend on the respiratory excitation, as Heymans *et al.* have shown that it also occurs in spinal animals on artificial respiration. These experiments indicated that cyanide has no direct stimulating effect on the vagus centres for the heart as doses 100 times greater

(10 mg), injected into the common carotid artery of dogs with the carotid sinus and aortic depressor nerves divided, did not alter the heart rate in any way.

The conclusion to be drawn from these experiments is that the slowing of the heart observed in the initial period of poisoning with hydrocyanic acid and its salts is the result of reflexes from carotid chemoreceptors the sensitivity of which to CN^- ions is much greater than the sensitivity of the vagus centres for the heart.

It may be thought that the slowing of the heart seen as a result of the action of cyanide on chemoreceptors might be a consequence of an increase of blood pressure and the reflexes from baroreceptors produced thereby, as well as the result of a direct reflex from the carotid bodies on the vagus nerve centres.

Special experiments were carried out in our laboratory in order to determine whether this indirect effect could be excluded (Nazarenko, 1958). An adrenolytic preparation, in Sympatholytin (N,N-dibenzyl-β-bromethylamine) in doses sufficient to abolish vasoconstrictor sympathetic impulses (0·8 ml of a 1% solution), was injected into decerebrate cats before the injection of cyanide. Potassium cyanide injected intravenously produced no pressor reflex but continued to cause slowing of the heart, so that the latter could be regarded as due exclusively to the direct reflex from carotid chemoreceptors on the vagus nerve centres.

Vascular Reflexes

Heymans *et al.* (1932) devoted one of their investigations to vascular reflexes developing in response to the action of chemical substances on the carotid sinuses. The experiments were arranged in the same way as for the investigation of respiratory and cardiac reflexes. Reflex increase of blood pressure could be observed even with a very weak potassium cyanide concentration acting on the carotid receptors. This occurred both when cyanide was injected intravenously into dogs with the nerve supply of the carotid sinuses and the aortic reflexogenic zone intact and when the poison was injected into the common carotid artery. Even extremely small doses of cyanide (0·01 mg) injected by the latter route produced a powerful but very transient pressor effect. This effect was not related to respiratory changes as it was also observed in curarized dogs on artificial respiration. When the same doses of cyanide were injected into the blood stream beyond the carotid sinus, the blood pressure did not rise. According to Heymans' experiments, only doses of cyanide 1000 times greater (10 mg) have a direct excitatory effect on the vasomotor centre. In experiments on two dogs with crossed circulations the injection of 10 mg potassium cyanide into the blood stream going to the brain of the dog with its sinuses denervated led to increase of blood pressure in its trunk. These experiments showed that, although the vasomotor centre could also respond by excitation to the direct action of large doses of cyanide, its sensitivity for hydrocyanic acid ions was much less than that of the carotid chemoreceptors.

Further investigations established that reflexes from the chemoreceptors to the vasomotor centre lead both to increase of blood pressure and to redistribution of blood and changes in the volume rate of flow in various vascular regions.

Bernthal (1932, 1934, 1938) showed that, when sodium cyanide acted on carotid sinuses which were supplied with heparinized blood, reduction in the minute volume was observed in the dog's subclavian artery. In these experiments the rate of flow was recorded thermoelectrically; the blood pressure was artificially maintained at a constant level and the vagus nerves were divided in order to exclude any indirect effects from blood pressure and vagus nerves.

When the cyanide solution was perfused through the carotid sinuses, the reduction in the volume rate of flow in the vessels of an extremity only lasted some tens of seconds, after which time blood flow returned to normal, or even above normal when the perfusion of cyanide ended.

Bernthal and also Heymans *et al.* (1935) likewise observed reduction of the volume rate of flow as a result of reflexes produced by the action of cyanide on the carotid chemoreceptors in the femoral artery of the dog. Using the same thermoelectric method, Bernthal and Schwind (1945) examined the reflex effect from the carotid chemoreceptors on the rate of blood flow in the intestinal vessels. In this region too the blood flow was reduced as a result of reflexes produced by the action of cyanide on the carotid chemoreceptors.

The constriction of the abdominal vessels and the vessels in the extremities together with the general rise of blood pressure will obviously lead to a redistribution of the blood in favour of the cerebral vessels and the vessels of the heart, in which the rate of blood flow must then be increased.

Using the thermoelectric method of Rein, Zakusov (1938) showed that the minute volume of blood flow through the kidneys, unlike the flow in the intestinal vessels, was not appreciably changed by the action of cyanides on the carotid chemoreceptors.

Reflex Erythrocytosis

An increase in the number of red cells in the blood is known to be one of the constant reactions to oxygen deficiency. This led us to examine the effect that cyanides had on the number of red cells in the peripheral blood and the part that reflexes from the carotid chemoreceptors played in this effect. This investigation was carried out by Belen'kii and Stroikov (1950, 1952).

The experiments were carried out on decerebrate cats. Potassium cyanide was injected into the femoral vein as a $0 \cdot 1$–$1 \cdot 0\%$ solution in amounts of from $0 \cdot 05$ to $1 \cdot 1$ mg/kg. Blood for red cell counts was taken from the cat's tail immediately before injection and again at the height of the dyspnoea following the injection, that is when the phenomena produced by reflexes from the carotid chemoreceptors were fully developed. There were in all sixteen experiments (Table 1).

In thirteen of the sixteen experiments the injection of potassium cyanide led to an increase in the number of red cells in the peripheral blood by an average of $17 \cdot 1\%$ (9–39%); in one experiment the red cell count was unchanged and in two there were slight reductions. In these last two experiments subsequent change of the cyanide dose led to the usual erythrocytosis.

The acute tissue hypoxia produced by the injection of cyanide thus leads to increase of the number of red cells in the peripheral blood.

In the experiments to determine what part the carotid chemoreceptors played in this reaction cyanide was injected intravenously into decerebrate cats in which the sensitivity of the carotid chemoreceptors had previously been abolished by infiltration of the tissue surrounding the carotid sinuses with 1% novocain solution. Altogether, there were ten experiments on animals on which the effect of cyanide had been tested with the carotid sinuses

TABLE 1

EFFECT OF INTRAVENOUS POTASSIUM CYANIDE ON THE NUMBER
OF RED CELLS IN THE PERIPHERAL BLOOD

No. of experiment	Initial red cell count $\times 10^3/\mu l$	Dose of KCN (mg/kg)	Red cell count after injection of KCN $\times 10^3/\mu l$	Percentage change in red cell count
1	10750	0·50	12750	+18·6
2	10660	0·19	11640	+ 9·2
3	8230	1·10	8220	− 0·1
4	6420	0·10	7070	+10·1
5	8730	0·20	9520	+ 9·0
6	8580	0·20	9680	+12·8
7	9170	0·19	8400	− 8·4
	7980	0·05	9010	+12·9
8	9570	0·10	9840	+14·8
9	7930	0·10	9680	+22·0
10	5860	0·10	7770	+32·6
11	7200	0·10	7730	+ 7·4
12	9780	0·10	8880	− 9·2
	8780	0·06	7910	− 9·9
	7120	0·16	9300	+30·6
13	8370	0·10	9480	+13·2
14	6860	0·05	9500	+38·4
15	7360	0·10	8630	+17·2
16	9260	0·10	10860	+17·2

functioning. After applying procaine to the sinus, blood was taken for red cell counts and the cat was then given, by intravenous injection, the same dose of potassium cyanide as before procaine administration and further red cell counts were carried out.

The test for the complete abolition of sensitivity in the carotid chemoreceptors was the absence of any respiratory reaction in the animal to the injection of cyanide. The results of these experiments, which are given in Table 2, show that the red cell response to cyanide was reduced, abolished or even reversed in eight of ten experiments after "pharmacological denervation" of the sinuses.

It follows, therefore, that the chemoreceptors of the carotid

TABLE 2

EFFECT OF INTRAVENOUS POTASSIUM CYANIDE ON THE PERIPHERAL RED CELL COUNT BEFORE AND AFTER PROCAINE TREATMENT OF THE CAROTID SINUSES

No. of experiment	Before procaine			After procaine		
	Initial red cell count $\times 10^3/\mu l$	Red cell count after injection of KCN $\times 10^3/\mu l$	Percentage change	Initial red cell count $\times 10^3/\mu l$	Red cell count after injection of KCN $\times 10^3/\mu l$	Percentage change
1	10750	12750	+18·6	12428	10610	−14·6
2	10660	11640	+9·2	10380	12140	+17·0
3	8230	8220	−0·1	7250	7940	+9·5
4	6420	7070	+10·1	7240	7420	+2·5
5	8730	9528	+9·0	9780	9200	−5·9
6	8580	9680	+12·8	10710	10240	−4·4
7	7980	9010	+12·9	8240	7990	−3·0
8	8570	9840	+14·8	7960	8390	+5·4
9	7930	9680	+22·0	8900	9400	+5·6
10	5860	7770	+32·6	7720	7800	+1·0

body undoubtedly take part in the production of erythrocytosis in response to cyanide action.

The results of Belen'kii and Stroikov's experiments would, however, indicate that other mechanisms are also concerned in this reaction as the erythrocytosis was not always abolished by procaine treatment of the sinuses; Table 2 shows that in two experiments the increase in the number of red cells after the injection of cyanide was even more pronounced after procainization of the sinuses than before. It is, therefore, quite probable that reflexes originating from other reflexogenic zones are partly responsible for the erythrocytosis produced by tissue hypoxia.

The aortic chemoreceptors apparently take part in this reaction. In Experiment No. 8 (Table 2) procaine treatment of the carotid sinuses did not completely abolish the erythrocytosis produced by the injection of cyanide. The cat's vagi were then divided and its aortic receptors were thus excluded. No increase in the number of red cells followed a subsequent injection of cyanide; the count was in fact slightly reduced.

These experiments do not exclude the possibility that the direct effect of the poison on nerve centres may also play a part in the production of erythrocytosis by cyanide.

Belen'kii and Stroikov sought to obtain convincing proof of the presence of a reflex mechanism for the production of erythrocytosis by the action of cyanide on the carotid chemoreceptors in perfusion experiments on the carotid sinus of decerebrate cats.

The first sample of blood for the red cell count was taken from the cats when pure Ringer–Locke solution was passing through the sinus, and the second was taken at the height of the dyspnoea which developed when the sinus was perfused with potassium cyanide solution. Table 3 shows that in all fourteen experiments without exception the passage of cyanide through the isolated sinus produced appreciable increase in the number of red cells in the peripheral blood.

Belen'kii and Stroikov's experiments thus proved that reflexes from the carotid chemoreceptors undoubtedly take part in the production of erythrocytosis in the acute tissue hypoxia caused by cyanides.

The rapidity with which the reflex erythrocytosis developed when cyanide was injected suggests that the mechanism of this

TABLE 3

CHANGES IN THE NUMBER OF RED CELLS IN THE PERIPHERAL BLOOD
PRODUCED BY THE ACTION OF KCN ON THE ISOLATED CAROTID SINUS

No. of experiment	Initial red cell count $\times 10^3/\mu l$	KCN concentration	Red cell count during perfusion with KCN $\times 10^3/\mu l$	Percentage change in the red cell count
17	7810	10^{-5}	9830	$+25 \cdot 9$
18	8190	10^{-5}	9170	$+11 \cdot 9$
19	6730	10^{-5}	7880	$+11 \cdot 9$
20	6840	10^{-5}	8010	$+17 \cdot 0$
21	8730	10^{-5}	9300	$+ 6 \cdot 5$
27	9990	10^{-5}	11340	$+13 \cdot 6$
29	9330	10^{-5}	10300	$+ 9 \cdot 3$
22	8710	2×10^{-5}	13810	$+58 \cdot 5$
23	10740	2×10^{-5}	12700	$+18 \cdot 2$
24	9860	2×10^{-5}	11240	$+14 \cdot 0$
25	7780	2×10^{-5}	9080	$+18 \cdot 0$
26	6930	2×10^{-5}	7810	$+11 \cdot 3$
28	9700	2×10^{-5}	10230	$+ 5 \cdot 5$
30	6650	2×10^{-5}	8760	$+14 \cdot 5$

reaction is a mobilization of the red cells from blood depots. The spleen is known to be a very important blood depot. The blood deposited in the spleen differs from the circulating blood in having a much higher content of formed elements. As contraction of the spleen is undoubtedly under nervous control, it could naturally be postulated that reflex contraction of the spleen is responsible for the erythrocytosis associated with excitation of the carotid bodies by cyanide.

This hypothesis was tested by Belen'kii and Stroikov in experiments on cats in which the carotid sinus was perfused with potassium cyanide solution before and after removal of the animal's spleen.

Perfusion of the sinus with potassium cyanide after splenectomy reduced the number of red cells in the peripheral blood in all experiments (Table 4). It was, therefore, proved that the discharge of its red cells by the spleen into the blood was the basis of the

TABLE 4

EFFECT OF SPLENECTOMY ON REFLEX ERYTHROCYTOSIS INDUCED BY CYANIDE

No. of experiment	Before splenectomy			After splenectomy		
	Initial red cell count $\times 10^3/\mu l$	Red cell count during perfusion with KCN $\times 10^3/\mu l$	Percentage change	Initial red cell count $\times 10^3/\mu l$	Red cell count during perfusion with KCN $\times 10^3/\mu l$	Percentage change
17	7810	9830	+ 25·9	7410	7530	+ 1·6
18	8190	9170	+ 11·9	8470	7100	−16·1
19	6730	7880	+ 17·0	6620	6470	− 2·3
20	6840	8010	+ 17·1	7350	6990	− 4·9
21	8730	9300	+ 6·5	8180	8010	− 2·0
22	8710	13810	+ 58·5	9710	7940	−18·2
23	10740	12700	+ 18·2	10430	9530	− 8·6
24	9860	11240	+ 14·0	9530	8750	− 8·2
25	7780	9080	+ 18·0	7640	7110	− 8·9

reflex erythrocytosis associated with the action of cyanide on the carotid chemoreceptors.

Since the muscle fibres of the spleen have a sympathetic nerve supply, it can be assumed that the reflex effects from the carotid bodies on the spleen are produced either directly through these nerve fibres or indirectly by adrenaline mobilized from the suprarenal glands as the result of a reflex originating in the chemoreceptors of the carotid bodies.

That the receptors for catecholamines in the spleen are concerned in its reaction to the excitation of the carotid bodies produced by cyanide was proved by Belen'kii and Stroikov in experiments with an adrenolytic preparation, Sympatholytin (N,N-dibenzyl-β-bromethylamine).

Sympatholytin was injected in a dose of 1 mg/kg. After the injection both the intravenous injection of potassium cyanide and perfusion of the isolated sinus with potassium cyanide solution produced a much smaller increase in the red cell count than before injection of Sympatholytin.

To sum up the results of these investigations by Belen'kii and Stroikov, it may be considered as proved that the action of cyanide on the carotid chemoreceptors leads to reflex erythrocytosis and that the immediate cause of this erythrocytosis is contraction of the spleen, in which its sympathetic nerve supply is involved.

Reflex Increase of Adrenomedullary Secretion

Reflex hyperadrenalinaemia resulting from the action of cyanides on the carotid sinuses was first noted by Petropavlovskaya (1953). The test for increased adrenaline solution used in her experiments was increase of blood sugar. Muller and Stephenson had already shown in 1937 that the hyperglycaemia produced by hydrocyanic acid was due to increased adrenaline secretion as it did not occur in adrenalectomized animals. Petropavlovskaya found that the increased discharge of adrenaline from the suprarenal glands, leading to the increase of blood sugar, was the result of the action of cyanide on the carotid chemoreceptors. In her experiments hyperglycaemia lasting more than an hour developed on the intravenous injection of potassium cyanide 0·1 mg/kg into non-anaesthetized dogs. Injection of the same dose of potassium cyanide into a dog in which the carotid sinuses had been denervated did not produce any appreciable change in the blood sugar. Integrity of the carotid sinus nerve supply is, therefore, an invariable condition for the development of hyperglycaemia as a result of the action of cyanide.

A further analysis of the part played by carotid chemoreceptors in the hyperglycaemia produced by cyanides was carried out by Petropavlovskaya on decerebrate cats. The intravenous injection of potassium cyanide in doses of from 0·05 to 0·1 mg/kg produced an increase of blood sugar lasting 1 or 2 hr in decerebrate cats with the nerve supply of the carotid sinuses intact. After 2 hr when the blood sugar had returned to normal, the sinuses were denervated and the intravenous injection of the same dose of potassium cyanide was repeated. In all six experiments of this kind the injection of cyanide after denervation of the carotid bodies had no effect on the blood sugar level. Perfusion of the isolated sinus in decerebrate cats was used in an effort to obtain direct proof of a reflex mechanism for the effect of cyanide on the blood sugar level. Potassium cyanide solution, 0·4 ml of a 1:10,000 solution, was injected into the Ringer–Locke solution passing through the isolated sinus. The violent dyspnoea which developed after injection proved that the carotid chemoreceptors were functionally active. Blood for sugar estimation was taken from the femoral vein. In all four experiments the action of cyanide on the isolated carotid sinuses increased the sugar content of the blood by 28–26%, or to about the same extent as in the experiments in which cyanide had been injected intravenously (Fig. 6).

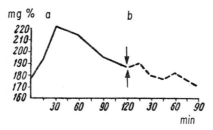

Fig. 6. Decerebrate cat. Change in the sugar content of the blood (mg per cent) on the intravenous injection of potassium cyanide (0·05 mg/kg).
a—before denervation of the carotid sinuses. b—after denervation.

The conclusion that can be drawn from these investigations is that the hyperglycaemia produced by cyanide is the result of reflexes from the carotid chemoreceptors. As the immediate cause of the cyanide-induced hyperglycaemia is an increased discharge of adrenaline into the blood, these experiments afford proof of reflex hyperadrenalinaemia produced by cyanide acting on carotid chemoreceptors.

This conclusion has been completely confirmed experimentally by Poskalenko (1955) who used different indicators for assessment of increase of adrenomedullary secretion. Her experiments were also carried out by perfusion of the isolated carotid sinus in decerebrate cats but the indicators of hyperadrenalinaemia used were contraction of the nictitating membrane and increase of blood pressure. In order to increase the cat's sensitivity to adrenaline it was given an intravenous injection of 8–10 mg cocaine and the superior cervical sympathetic ganglion on the side on which the contractions of the nictitating membrane were recorded was removed. The contractions of the nictitating membrane and blood pressure in the common carotid artery were recorded simultaneously. In sixteen of the seventeen experiments carried out in this way the injection of potassium cyanide (0·2–0·5 ml of 1:5000 and 1:10,000 solutions) into the stream of fluid perfusing the isolated sinus was followed by contraction of the denervated nictitating membrane and rise of blood pressure. As the nictitating membrane was sympathectomized, direct reflexes on it were excluded. Its contraction, therefore, pointed to increase of adrenaline or of adrenaline-like substances in the blood.

It has long been established that there is a reflex connexion between baroreceptors and the adrenal medulla. In 1934 Euler and Liljestrand had shown that compression of the carotid arteries led to increase of adrenomedullary secretion. This has been confirmed by other authors (Holtz and Schumann, 1949; Brauner et al., 1950). Carotid chemoreceptor excitation is thus similar in its effect on adrenomedullary secretion and in respect of some other reactions to the abolition of tonic impulses from carotid baroreceptors.

The question then arises as to the complete identity of the impulses transmitted to the suprarenal glands in these two forms of reaction that take their origin in the carotid sinus. One way in which this question can be settled is to examine the nature of the secretion produced by reflexes from chemoreceptors and baro-receptors respectively.

We know that noradrenaline enters the blood along with adrenaline from the adrenal medulla. The suprarenal secretion contains a particularly high percentage of noradrenaline in cats. The discharge of noradrenaline, like that of adrenaline, increases in response to splanchnic nerve stimulation (Bulbring and Burn, 1949; Gaddum and Lemberg, 1949) and also when acetylcholine acts on the suprarenal glands (Yemel'yanova, 1954).

It is stated in the literature that some central impulses cause mainly adrenaline secretion and others one of mainly norad-renaline. Electrical stimulation of some parts of the hypothala-mic region leads to adrenaline secretion mainly and stimulation of other parts to predominant secretion of noradrenaline (Malmejac, 1959).

In investigating the reflex effects from the carotid sinus region on the catecholamine secretion of the adrenal medulla, we attempted to compare the secretions produced by lowering the pressure in the sinus and excitation of chemoreceptors with cyanide respectively, each time determining the proportions of noradrenaline in the secretion.

The first part of this study was carried out by Poskalenko (1955). In her experiments on decerebrate cats adrenaline was injected intravenously in order to compare the effects with those produced by the injection of potassium cyanide into the fluid perfusing the carotid sinuses. It was noted that the dose of adrenaline producing the same pressor effect as the action of cyanide on the carotid sinus gave a much more active contraction of the nictitating membrane than that produced by the action of cyanide. In other words, the action of cyanide on the sinus yielded a relatively weaker contraction of the nictitating membrane and a relatively greater pressor effect than the intravenous injection of adrenaline. This difference indicated that reflex excitation of the suprarenal gland apparently increased the discharge of noradrenaline as well as adrenaline into the blood, as the former is known to have a more powerful pressor effect and a weaker action on the nictitating membrane.

In order to know that the reflexes produced by the action of cyanide on the carotid chemoreceptors did actually lead to the discharge of noradrenaline as well as adrenaline from the supra-renals, the effects on the nictitating membrane and vessels were studied when these structures were denervated to prevent direct reflex reactions mediated by sympathetic nerve fibres. This was done in the next series of experiments.

The nictitating membrane and both hindlegs were sympathecto-mized in decerebrate cats; the sympathectomy of the legs was by bilateral removal of the lumbar sympathetic chains. One leg was inserted into a plethysmograph for registration of vasoconstriction. Changes in the volume of the limb were recorded by observation of the movement of fluid in a capillary tube connected with the plethy-smograph. The potassium cyanide was injected into the fluid per-fusing the isolated sinus. As in the preceding series of experiments, adrenaline was injected intravenously for comparison in doses producing vasoconstriction approximately equal to that observed under the action of cyanide on the sinus.

In all six experiments carried out in this way adrenaline pro-duced more powerful contractions of the nictitating membrane than the passage of cyanide through the sinus.

Thus differences were also observed in the relative strengths of the reactions of nictitating membrane and vessels in response to the intravenous injection of adrenaline and in response to the substances which were discharged from the suprarenal glands when cyanide acted on the carotid chemoreceptors in the conditions of these experiments, in which all possibility of direct sinus reflexes to the vessels had been removed. When, therefore, the suprarenal gland is stimulated reflexly from the carotid bodies, its medulla secretes both adrenaline and noradrenaline, a substance with a very similar action.

The relative proportions of noradrenaline and adrenaline in the adrenal secretion produced by lowering the pressure in the sinus and by hypoxic excitation of the carotid chemoreceptors were investigated by Malygina (1961). These experiments were carried out on decerebrate cats. Excitation of the carotid bodies was produced by the injection of small doses of potassium cyanide ($0\cdot05$–$0\cdot25$ ml of $0\cdot01\%$ solution) into the carotid artery through a cannula inserted into the thyroid artery. Baroreceptor reaction to reduction of pressure was produced by compression of the carotid. Adrenomedullary secretion and the proportions of adrenaline and noradrenaline excreted were assessed, as in the preceding experiments, from vascular reactions in a denervated leg (plethysmography) and from the contraction of the denervated nictitating membrane. Cocaine was injected intravenously to increase the cats' sensitivity to catecholamines.

When a dose of cyanide was chosen which, acting on the carotid bodies, produced the same vasoconstriction as compression of the carotid artery, the contraction of the nictitating membrane in the reflex from the chemoreceptors was usually more powerful than that produced by compression of the common carotid artery. The results of these experiments are given in Table 5.

Comparison of these results with the results of the experiments described earlier leads to the conclusion that both adrenaline and noradrenaline are discharged into the blood in response both to reduction of pressure in the carotid sinuses and to carotid chemoreceptor excitation by a hypoxic poison. The secretion of adrenaline is relatively greater in excitation of the carotid chemoreceptors and the secretion of noradrenaline is relatively increased in reactions to reduction of blood pressure.

The results of Malygina's experiments are in complete agreement with published reports on the nature of the adrenal secretion in response to compression of a carotid artery. In the experiments of Holtz and Schumann (1949) compression of the carotid artery produced an increase of blood pressure and contraction of the spleen but did not increase blood sugar or arrest peristalsis. The intravenous injection of a small dose of adrenaline sufficient to produce the same contraction of the spleen as compression of the carotid artery was followed by arrest of peristalsis also. This did not occur when corresponding doses of noradrenaline were injected. Compression of the carotid artery after adrenalectomy did not produce contraction of the spleen. The authors conclude that the adrenal secretion resulting from compression of the carotid artery is mainly of noradrenaline and not adrenaline.

It should be remembered in connexion with the difference in the reaction of the suprarenal glands to compression of the carotid artery and to chemoreceptor excitation that noradrenaline has the more powerful vasoconstrictor effect and adrenaline is the stronger in its action on metabolism (mobilization of liver glycogen and tissue oxygen consumption).

The conclusions to be drawn from the experiments of Petropavlovskaya, Poskalenko and Malygina are that: (1) the action of cyanide on the carotid chemoreceptors leads to reflexly intensified adrenomedullary secretion producing hyperglycaemia and other typical catecholamine effects; and (2) there is simultaneous

TABLE 5

CONTRACTION OF THE NICTITATING MEMBRANE AND PLETHYSMOGRAPHIC FINDINGS

No. of experiment	Contraction of the nictitating membrane (mm)		Reduction in the volume of the extremity (hundredths of a millimetre)	
	Compression of common carotid artery	Injection of KCN	Compression of common carotid artery	Injection of KCN
1	1·0	2·5	20	22
2	1·0	2·0	10	13
3	2·0	3·0	18	20
4	2·0	3·0	30*	31*
5	2·0	4·0	28	30
6	7·0	6·0	100*	80*
7	1·5	1·5	48*	40*
8	1·5	2·0	40*	41*
	2·0	2·0	18	14
	1·0	5·0	15	25
9	1·5	1·0	15	10
	1·0	1·0	25	28
10	3·0	5·0	48*	48*
11	2·0	8·0	32	29
	1·5	—	28	—
12	3·0	5·0	43*	40*
13	1·0	2·0	15	11
14	1·0	2·0	10	20
15	1·0	2·0	7	8
16	1·0	2·0	11	10
17	3·0	3·0	33*	34*
18	1·0	2·0	15	15
19	1·5	3·0	10	12
20	4·0	6·0	50	53

* Experiments in which reduction of the volume of the limb was preceded by slight increase.

discharge of noradrenaline from the suprarenal gland but in less quantity than in the secretory activity of the adrenals produced by fall of pressure in the carotid sinuses.

Reflex Effects in the Hypophyseo-Adrenal system

The effect of cyanide on adrenocortical function and the importance of carotid chemoreceptors have been studied by Poskalenko (1958) (see also Anichkov et al., 1960). In experiments on rats the functional activity of the adrenal cortex was assessed from the ascorbic acid content of the suprarenal glands. Potassium cyanide solution was injected into the peritoneal cavity of the rats; the control animals received normal saline. Both experimental and control rats were killed by decapitation.

The intraperitoneal injection of potassium cyanide (3 mg/kg) lowered the ascorbic acid level in the suprarenals. Thirty minutes after the injection ascorbic acid had fallen by 20% (this difference in the ascorbic acid contents of the suprarenal glands in the experimental and control animals was found to be statistically significant). The reduction of the ascorbic acid content of the adrenals in response to the injection of potassium cyanide was the result of intensification of the hormonal activity of the hypophysis. This follows from the fact that injection of the same dose of cyanide into hypophysectomized rats did not produce any change in the ascorbic acid content of the suprarenal glands. Indeed, after injection of cyanide the ascorbic acid content of the adrenals was found to be higher in the hypophysectomized than in the control animals (Tables 6 and 7).

Similar experiments were also carried out on rats with the carotid bodies removed. Light ether anaesthesia was used and the operation was carried out with the aid of a binocular disecting microscope.

The removal of the carotid bodies was considered complete when no dyspnoea developed in response to the injection of cyanide. Table 8 shows that the average reduction of ascorbic acid content produced by potassium cyanide was only 5% more in the rats with the carotid bodies removed than in the control rats subjected to the same operation but given injections of normal saline. (This difference was not found to be statistically significant.)

Cyanide-induced reflexes from the carotid bodies were, therefore, the main cause of the increase in adrenocorticotropic hormone

TABLE 6

EFFECT OF KCN (3 mg/kg) ON THE ASCORBIC ACID CONTENT OF THE SUPRARENAL GLANDS IN NORMAL RATS

No. of experiment	Number of animals	Ascorbic acid content (mg %)	
		Control	30–40 min after injection of KCN
1	5	478	371
2	5	416	330
3	2	428	398
4	4	468	358
5	5	456	352
6	2	463	306
7	2	499	432
8	4	419	341
9	4	335	320
10	4	343	317
11	2	485	406
12	10	410	336
	Average	$433 \pm 15 \cdot 2$	$355 \pm 11 \cdot 3$

TABLE 7

EFFECT OF KCN (3 mg/kg) ON THE ASCORBIC ACID CONTENT OF THE SUPRARENAL GLANDS IN HYPOPHYSECTOMIZED RATS

No. of experiment	Number of animals	Ascorbic acid content (mg %)	
		Control	30–40 min after injection of KCN
1	1	475	549
2	2	630	660
3	1	406	420
4	2	455	465
5	2	447	444
	Average	482 ± 38	507 ± 43

secretion following the injection of potassium cyanide. Other less important factors are apparently also concerned in this effect. These probably include reflexes from other chemoreceptors sensitive to hypoxic poisons such as the aortic receptors, as well as reflexes arising from the peritoneum as a result of local irritation by the injected solution.

TABLE 8

EFFECT OF KCN (3 mg/kg) on the ASCORBIC ACID CONTENT OF THE SUPRARENAL GLANDS IN RATS WITH THE CAROTID BODIES REMOVED

No. of experiment	Number of animals	Ascorbic acid content (mg %)	
		Control	30–40 min after injection of KCN
1	1	341	332
2	1	344	344
3	2	505	476
4	2	453	415
5	2	496	451
6	2	446	429
	Average	430 ± 31	408 ± 24

Reflex involvement of the hypophyseo-adrenal system resulting from the action of cyanide on the carotid chemoreceptors was also demonstrated in experiments on decerebrate cats.

The indicator of adrenocortical activity employed was reduction in the number of eosinophils in the peripheral blood. Decerebration was effected at a level between the anterior and posterior corpora quadrigemina. The operation itself produced a certain degree of eosinopenia, but the number of eosinophils became more or less constant after an interval of about 2 hr, so that eosinophil counts could then be used to assess changes in the hormonal activity of the adrenal cortex.

Potassium cyanide was injected intravenously in doses of 0·1–0·4 mg/kg. A reduction in the number of eosinophils was observed 20–30 min after the injection of potassium cyanide in six out of seven cats. Only one of five decerebrate cats with the hypophysis removed exhibited slight reduction in the number of eosinophils with the same doses of cyanide. It would appear, therefore, that the eosinopenia produced by the intravenous injection of cyanide is an index of the excitation of the hypophyseo-adrenal system.

In order to determine whether this reaction was connected with the excitatory action of cyanide on the carotid chemoreceptors, these experiments were repeated on decerebrate cats in which the carotid sinuses were removed before the injection of cyanide (complete removal of the region of bifurcation of both carotid arteries). Cyanide produced no significant eosinopenia in any of five such cats; slight reduction in the percentage of eosinophils was noted in two and the number was even slightly increased in the others.

The conclusion can be drawn from these experiments that the excitation of the hypophyseo-adrenal system which develops in the stage of cyanide absorption is due to reflexes from the carotid chemoreceptors. Both the rat experiments and the cat experiments indicate that reflexes produced by the action of cyanides on the carotid chemoreceptors lead to discharge of adrenocorticotropic hormone which activates the hormonal activity of the adrenal cortex.

Reflex Effects on the Neurohypophysis

The spread of reflexes to the posterior pituitary lobe was first demonstrated by Belous in her pharmacological analysis of reflex control of the neurohypophysis (1952, 1953). It was shown that, in the dog, the intravenous injection of potassium cyanide or the inhalation of hydrocyanic gas led to postpituitary hypersecretion.

Belous carried out her investigations in chronic experiments on dogs with urinary fistulas. The diuresis which follows the introduction into the stomach of a large quantity of water (water diuresis) is known to be controlled by the neurohypophysis and can, therefore, be used as an index of its secretory activity. When posterior pituitary secretion increases, water diuresis is retarded. This was the index of neurohypophyseal secretion used by Belous.

She investigated the effects on posterior pituitary secretion of, among other pharmacologically active substances, hydrocyanic acid and potassium cyanide. Water, 50 ml/kg, was introduced into the dog's stomach before each experiment. The urine was then collected every 15 min. Potassium cyanide in dosage of 0·4–0·5 mg/kg was usually injected at the height of diuresis. This dose produced violent dyspnoea, tremor and, occasionally, an attack of transient convulsions in the dogs.

A porcelain vessel containing 2 ml 30% hydrochloric acid to which 1 ml 10% potassium cyanide solution was added immediately before its application to the dog's muzzle was used for the inhalation of hydrocyanic gas. Breathing of the gas thus formed for 20–30 sec produced attacks of violent panting in the dog.

Numerous experiments on dogs with the nerve supply to the carotid sinuses intact showed that the intravenous injection of potassium cyanide, like the breathing of hydrocyanic acid, led to arrest of water diuresis. The degree and duration of the arrest depended on the rapidity with which the poison was injected and on the individual sensitivities of the dogs. Control experiments on hypophysectomized dogs were carried out to determine whether the hypophysis was concerned in this antidiuretic effect of cyanides. Hypophysectomy was performed by the temporal route (see Karlik, 1939). The dog's hypophysis was removed 2 months before the experiment. The completeness of the hypophysectomy was subsequently confirmed by histological examination.

By the time of the experiment the polyurea exhibited by the dog in the period immediately following the operation had been replaced by reduction of water diuresis to below the normal level. Six experiments were carried out in which the usual dose of potassium cyanide was injected intravenously. In all these experiments, in contrast to what had been observed before hypophysectomy, the injection of potassium cyanide had no effect whatever on water diuresis.

In order to ensure that arrest of water diuresis could actually occur under these conditions generally and at this level of water diuresis, the hypophysectomized dog was given an intravenous injection of pituitrin, which had its usual inhibitory effect on urine secretion induced by water loading.

The fact that cyanide had no effect on water diuresis in the hypophysectomized dog indicates that the hypophysis is involved in the antidiuretic effect of cyanide. Cyanide apparently leads to an increase of posterior pituitary secretion and discharge of antidiuretic hormone (vasopressin).

It is natural to assume that this effect, like a number of others produced by cyanide, is the result of reflexes from the carotid chemoreceptors. Experiments to prove this were carried out on four dogs, the carotid bodies of which had been removed. Hering's nerves were divided simultaneously with removal of the carotid bodies. The bilateral operation was carried out under complete asepsis; the incision was sutured and the experiments were carried out when the wound had healed completely.

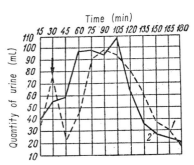

FIG. 7. Dog with chronic fistula of the urinary bladder. Water test (40 ml/kg). Diuresis curves. The arrow indicates the intravenous injection of potassium cyanide (0·4 mg/kg).
1—with the carotid bodies intact. 2—after their removal.

Nine experiments, in which potassium cyanide was injected intravenously, were carried out on four dogs with the carotid bodies removed. In three the same doses of potassium cyanide had been tested before denervation of the sinuses. In all these experiments potassium cyanide caused much less arrest of diuresis than in dogs with the carotid bodies and Hering's nerves intact. Potassium cyanide had no effect whatever on water diuresis in some of the experiments in which the sinuses had been denervated. The absence of the usual dyspnoea in these animals indicated that the carotid sinuses had been completely denervated.

The effect of sinus denervation on the antidiuretic action of potassium cyanide in the dogs is shown in Fig. 7.

It was thus established that, in addition to the neurohypophysis, the carotid bodies played a decisive part in the antidiuretic effect of cyanide. We conclude that this antidiuretic effect of cyanide is basically the result of reflexes from the carotid bodies on the neurohypophysis.

Thus when cyanide acts on the carotid chemoreceptors, reflexes evoking increased posterior pituitary secretion develop along with the other reflexes.

Gastrointestinal Reflexes

The effect of cyanide on the secretion and motor activity of the gastrointestinal tract and the part played by carotid sinus reflexes have been studied in our laboratory by Startsev (1958, 1959). He has shown that the intravenous injection of sodium cyanide (0·5 mg/kg) into unanaesthetized dogs is followed by a transient disturbance of the secretory and motor activity of the stomach, in addition to dyspnoea. These experiments were carried out on six dogs with various types of chronic gastrointestinal fistulas.

Sodium cyanide delayed the secretion of gastric juice in response to meat in the dog with a Pavlov gastric pouch. The inhibition of secretion was greatest during the first 15 min after the injection of cyanide. After 1 hr secretion was at the normal level. Arrest of secretion of gastric juice in response to sham feeding was also observed in an oesophagotomized dog after the injection of sodium cyanide.

Cyanide also affected the motor activity of the dog's stomach: there was transient arrest of the contractions of the empty stomach when it was in a state of periodic activity. This arrest began a few seconds after the cyanide injection and lasted for from 6 to 45 min in different experiments. The usual periodic activity of the empty stomach was then resumed and in some experiments the total number of contractions was even larger than in ordinary periods of activity.

The injection of sodium cyanide (0·5 mg/kg) into the carotid artery which had been exteriorized into a skin flap, towards the carotid sinus (all branches of the carotid artery with the exception of the lingual artery and the arterioles supplying the carotid bodies had previously been ligatured) was followed by intensified contractions of the empty stomach following the arrest. The powerful contraction in the empty stomach seen under these conditions probably due to the fact that the carotid body was exposed to a very high concentration of cyanide.

The digestive juices discharged from the duodenal fistula, a mixture of pancreatic juice and the bile which is discharged into the duodenum during the periods of activity in the empty stomach (periodic duodenal secretion), was reduced simultaneously with the inhibition of gastric motor activity.

On the other hand, there was no reduction of the secretion of intestinal juice in an isolated Thiry–Vella pouch.

The injection of cyanide had likewise no effect on the contractions of the ileum in the dog with a chronic fistula of this part of the intestine.

Experiments were carried out on the same dogs after denervation of their carotid sinuses in order to determine whether reflexes from the carotid chemoreceptors were concerned in the inhibition of gastric secretion and motor activity produced by cyanide. The denervation by division of Hering's nerves was carried out under aseptic conditions; the experiments were performed after the wound had healed completely.

Injection of the same doses of sodium cyanide into the dogs with their sinuses denervated had no effect whatever on the secretory activity or the contractile function of the stomach.

The inhibition of gastric activity produced by cyanide is apparently the result of reflexes arising from the carotid chemoreceptors.

The reflex effect of cyanide on intestinal motor activity resulting from stimulation of the cyanide on the carotid bodies was demonstrated by Startsev in experiments on decerebrate cats in which the isolated sinus was perfused.

The intestinal contractions were recorded mechanically by the Nikolayev–Subbotin method. Sodium or potassium cyanide was injected into the perfusion fluid in quantities of 1 ml of 1:1000 and 1:10,000 solution in the course of 3–6 sec. In most experiments (16 of 18) the injection of cyanide led to decreased contractions and a reduction of intestinal tone, lasting for from 10 sec to 30 min, after which the motor activity of the intestine generally increased again.

Comparative observations revealed that the inhibition of contractions induced by the action of cyanide on the isolated sinus was greater in the proximal than in the distal parts of the intestine. When the tissue surrounding the sinus had been infiltrated with procaine, the passage of sodium cyanide through the sinus had no effect on the intestinal contraction; the reflex nature of the reaction was thus confirmed.

Special experiments were carried out on cats which were both decerebrate and adrenalectomized. Sodium cyanide acting on the isolated sinus likewise inhibited intestinal contractions in these experiments.

This indicated that the increased adrenal secretion produced by reflexes from the carotid bodies was not the main cause of the intestinal inhibition observed.

To sum up these experiments on the influence of cyanide on gastrointestinal function, it can be stated that excitation of the carotid chemoreceptors by cyanide influences gastrointestinal motor activity and secretion reflexly. There is inhibition of both secretion and motor activity. Excitation sometimes follows the initial inhibition of the motor activity. The most powerful reflex effects on secretion and motor activity are observed in the stomach and the effects produced in the more distant parts of the intestine are weaker.

HYDROGEN SULPHIDE AND OTHER SULPHIDES

Warburg (1946) was the first to show that hydrogen sulphide and its salts are, like cyanides, capable of blocking iron-containing enzymes and thus suppressing oxidation processes in the tissues. Hydrogen sulphide and its salts must, therefore, be regarded as hypoxic poisons.

The decisive part played by reflexes from the carotid chemoreceptors in the respiratory stimulation produced by sulphides was first demonstrated by Heymans et al. (1931a) by the same methods used to demonstrate the importance of the carotid chemoreceptors in the action of cyanides. Their experiments showed that the injection of a small dose of sodium sulphide into the common carotid artery of a dog in which the sinus retained its normal nerve supply produced an immediate and powerful respiratory excitation, whereas the injection of considerably larger doses of the same poison into the carotid artery of animal in which the sinus had been denervated had no immediate effect on respiration. Nor was respiratory excitation produced by the injection of sulphide into the internal carotid artery or the vertebral artery. Large doses of sulphides injected into these arteries merely produced respiratory depression. It was concluded from these experiments that the respiratory excitation produced by sulphides was due to a reflex from the carotid bodies. This conclusion was confirmed by experiments in which sodium sulphide was injected intravenously into dogs with the carotid and aortic reflexogenic zones denervated. In such animals the intravenous injection of sodium sulphide merely produced very slight respiratory excitation or depression.

Finally, Heymans *et al.* carried out experiments in which the isolated carotid sinuses of the dog B (recipient) were connected up to the circulation of the dog A (donor). When sodium sulphide (15 ml of 0·2% solution) was injected into a vein of the donor dog violent respiratory excitation was observed in the dog B. Yet, the injection of even a slightly larger dose of sulphide into a vein of the dog B did not produce any respiratory excitation. The vagus nerves in the dog B were then divided to abolish reflexes from the aortic zone.

Heymans *et al.* (1931c) likewise demonstrated that reflex slowing of the heart resulted, along with the respiratory excitation, from the action of sulphides on the carotid chemoreceptors.

Slowing of the heart was seen in dogs only when the sulphide (0·2 mg) was injected into the common carotid artery and when the sinus nerves were intact; there was no sign of slowing when the same dose was injected into the common carotid artery after the sinuses had been denervated or when it was injected directly into the internal carotid or vertebral artery, that is, beyond the sinus.

These experiments indicated that the cardiac centres of the vagus nerve were only slightly sensitive to sulphides: the injection into the internal carotid artery or the vertebral artery of doses fifty times greater (10 mg) than that effective when applied on the sinus had no effect on the cardiac rate.

These same authors, in order to exclude any possible indirect effects on the heart rate from changes in blood pressure or respiration, carried out experiments on dogs in which the neck was divided and the head communicated with the trunk only through the carotid arteries, the jugular veins and the vagus nerves. The dog was on artificial respiration. Respiratory and vascular reflexes could not occur under these conditions. The injection of small doses of sodium sulphide (0·2 mg) into a common carotid artery caused a sudden slowing of the heart in these experiments.

Studying pressor reflexes from the carotid chemoreceptors on the vasomotor centre, Heymans *et al.* (1932) investigated the effects of a number of substances including sulphides. They found that sulphides, like other substances stimulating chemoreceptors, produced a reflex increase of blood pressure. Such a reflex developed when very small doses (0·2 mg) were injected into the common carotid artery of dogs anaesthetized with chloralose, with the nerve supply to the sinus, intact and all the main branches tied. The reflex pressor effect of sulphides had no connexion with the respiratory excitation, as it was also observed in curarized animals on artificial respiration.

When sulphide was injected directly into the internal carotid artery and did not, therefore, pass through the sinus, a dose fifty times greater (10 mg) did not result in any rise of blood pressure.

Heymans and his co-workers thus proved convincingly that sulphides, like cyanides, excite carotid chemoreceptors and thereby produce reflex respiratory excitation, bradycardia and increase of blood pressure.

The results obtained in Heymans' laboratory on the selective action of sulphides on the carotid chemoreceptors were subsequently confirmed by other authors (Owen and Gesell, 1932; Winder and Winder, 1933). The latter authors found that carotid chemoreceptor excitation, as manifested by reflex dyspnoea, was observed when extremely small doses of sodium sulphide (0·006 mg/kg) were injected into a common carotid artery. When the carotid and aortic zones had been denervated, respiratory excitation could only be produced by very large doses of sulphide; the authors explained this effect by direct action of sulphide on the respiratory centre. The dyspnoea which developed under these conditions was somewhat delayed and was distinguished by its comparative mildness and long duration. The stimulating effect of sulphides on the carotid receptors and the part played by the resultant reflexes in the development of the dyspnoea has been confirmed by Verdonk (1937, 1939, 1941) and Nekhoroshev (1948). The latter showed that, when the carotid sinus region had been infiltrated with procaine the intravenous injection of sulphides failed to produce the usual increase of blood pressure.

E

The effect of sulphides on the carotid chemoreceptors has been studied in our laboratory by Zburzhinskii (1958, 1960, 1961). Most of his experiments were carried out on decerebrate cats. The injection of from 0·5 to 4·0 mg/kg sodium sulphide into the femoral vein in decerebrate cats was followed by powerful though temporary respiratory excitation and increase of blood pressure. This primary pressor phase was followed by a fall of blood pressure. Injection of the same doses of sulphide into cats with the sinuses denervated failed to produce either respiratory excitation or the first pressor phase of blood pressure change.

In experiments on decerebrate cats in which the isolated carotid sinus was perfused with Ring–Locke solution the injection of sodium sulphide (0·1–0·5 ml of 0·1% solution) into the perfusion fluid produced reflex respiratory excitation and rise of blood pressure. These experiments of Zburzhinskii on cats thus afforded complete confirmation of the experiments of Heymans *et al.* on dogs.

In addition to respiratory and blood pressure reflexes Zburzhinskii studied reflex changes in the number of red cells and in the sugar content of the peripheral blood produced by the action of sulphides on the carotid chemoreceptors.

The most convincing proof of reflex increase in the number of red cells in the blood resulting from the action of sulphides on the carotid chemoreceptors was obtained by Zburzhinskii in experiments in which the isolated carotid sinus was perfused in decerebrate cats.

Sodium sulphide in doses of from 0·1 to 1·0 mg was injected into the perfusion fluid. The blood for red cell counts was taken from the femoral artery. The first blood sample (before the injection of sodium sulphide) was taken 15–20 min after perfusion of the sinus with Ringer–Locke solution had been started. Sodium sulphide solution was injected into the perfusion fluid immediately after the blood had been taken, and a second blood sample was collected at the height of the dyspnoea which developed. Table 9 shows that the action of sodium sulphide on the isolated sinus led to increase in the number of red cells in the circulating blood.

Zburzhinskii's experiments indicate that this reflex may partly explain the erythrocytosis sometimes observed to follow the absorption of hydrogen sulphide or its salt and which has been noted earlier by some authors studying the effects of sulphur baths.

Zburzhinskii also observed erythrocytosis in most of the experiments on normal rabbits and decerebrate cats breathing hydrogen sulphide. A mixture of hydrogen sulphide and air (the mixture contained 0·09% H_2S by volume) was breathed from a Douglas bag. Blood was taken for red cell counts before administration and in the fifth minutes of the inhalation of hydrogen sulphide. The inhalation of hydrogen sulphide produced erythrocytosis in almost half the experiments on decerebrate cats with the nerve supply of the

TABLE 9

REFLEXES CHANGES IN THE RED CELL COUNT ON THE INJECTION OF Na_2S
INTO THE ISOLATED CAROTID SINUS

Initial number of red cells (thousands)	Number of red cells after injection (thousands)	Percentage change
9870	10810	+ 9·5
9940	10880	+ 8·5
12760	14340	+12·4
8930	9600	+ 7·5
7100	8060	+13·5
9540	11900	+24·7
6400	7350	+14·8

carotid sinuses intact. The experimental animals' carotid sinuses were denervated 1 hr after the first administration and, after a certain interval, a blood sample was again taken and the 5-min inhalation of the same gaseous mixture was repeated. In none of the experiments did hydrogen sulphide produce erythrocytosis after denervation of the sinuses.

Experiments were carried out to demonstrate the role of the spleen in the sulphide-induced erythrocytosis. In the splenectomized cats hydrogen sulphide produced no erythrocytosis and the number of red cells was in fact reduced in most cases (Table 10).

It follows from Zburzhinskii's experiments that reflexes from the carotid chemoreceptors are involved in the erythrocytosis produced by hydrogen sulphide; they lead to contraction of the spleen and discharge of red cells into the general circulation. An important point is that, unlike in the experiments in which the sinus was perfused, erythrocytosis was not seen by any means in all the experiments in which hydrogen sulphide was inhaled. It is probable that when hydrogen sulphide is absorbed reflexes from the carotid bodies develop which tend to produce erythrocytosis, but there are also reactions of opposite trend, causing dilution of the blood and so masking the erythrocytosis to some extent.

TABLE 10

CHANGE IN THE ERYTHROCYTIC REACTION TO H_2S AFTER SPLENECTOMY

No. of experiment	Percentage change in the red cell count produced by inhalation of hydrogen sulphide	
	Before splenectomy	After splenectomy
1	+37·9	+ 1·7
2	− 2·6	−10·2
3	+ 1·9	− 2·1
4	+20·5	−13·8
5	− 3·0	− 7·3
6	+ 1·0	−13·0
7	+ 4·9	− 8·1
8	+ 9·0	− 2·5

Splenectomy experiments revealed such a reaction very clearly, with reflex erythrocytosis being then excluded. Similar observations were made when the cyanide-induced erythrocytosis was studied (Belen'kii and Stroikov, 1950, 1952).

This double type of change produced by hydrogen sulphide in the red blood cell picture is also reflected in the literature: some authors draw attention to the erythrocytosis produced by sulphur baths while others describe reduction in the number of red cells in the same connotation.

Zburzhinskii carried out another series of experiments on decerebrate cats in order to investigate the effect of hydrogen sulphide on the blood sugar. The actual process of decerebration itself is known to cause hyperglycaemia; no experiment was, therefore, started less than 3 hr after decerebration. The blood for sugar estimations was taken from the femoral artery. The first sample was taken immediately before the inhalation, the second immediately after a 5-min inhalation of hydrogen sulphide and successive samples were then taken every 15 min in the first hour and every 30 min in the second.

Inhalation of hydrogen sulphide had a hyperglycaemic effect in all eight such experiments.

Six parallel experiments were carried out on decerebrate cats with the carotid sinuses denervated. The hydrogen sulphide merely produced slight hyperglycaemia in four of these and in two the sugar level was reduced. It may be concluded that reflexes from the carotid chemoreceptors are concerned in the development of the hyperglycaemia caused by hydrogen sulphide and its salts.

As reflex effects on the suprarenal glands from the carotid bodies played a special part in the reflex hyperglycaemia produced by cyanides, it was natural to assume that the same mechanism would by the dominant one in the hyperglycaemia produced by the action of sulphides on chemoreceptors. Experiments were designed to test this. In view of Fedorchuk's findings (1954) in experiments with nicotine that the spread of reflexes from the carotid sinuses to the suprarenal glands was mainly unilateral, Zburzhinskii removed the carotid sinus on one side and the suprarenal gland on the other in some of his experiments. Inhalation of hydrogen sulphide after this operation produced only very slight increase of blood sugar or even reduction.

It can thus be regarded as proved that reflexes from the carotid chemoreceptors to the suprarenal glands are concerned in the development of hyperglycaemia induced by hydrogen sulphide.

Our co-worker Ryzhenkov (1959) has shown that the hormonal activity of the adrenal cortex is increased in sulphide poisoning and that reflexes from the carotid bodies play a part in this reaction (see also Anichkov et al., 1960).

Rats, decerebrate cats and unanaesthetized dogs were used in these experiments.

In the rat experiments the index of the hormonal activity of the adrenal cortex was reduction in the ascorbic acid content of the suprarenal glands. A solution of sodium sulphide (15–20 mg/kg) was injected intraperitoneally into the rats. These doses produced dyspnoea, indicative of carotid chemoreceptor excitation. Ten rats were used in each experiment; five were given sodium sulphide and five control animals received saline. The rats were killed by decapitation at various periods thereafter. Ascorbic acid was determined in the ten suprarenal glands of the five rats in each group. In all there were twenty such experiments involving 100 experimental and 100 control animals. Rats were killed after 0·5, 1, 2 and 4 hr. Table 11 shows the average ascorbic acid content of the suprarenals of the experimental and control rats in each series. In all series the ascorbic acid content was lower in the experimental rats than in the controls. This reduction was greatest 60 min after the injection of sodium sulphide; the difference between the ascorbic acid content of the suprarenals in the experimental and control rats in this series was statistically significant.

As reduction in the ascorbic acid content of the suprarenals is one of the signs of intensified hormonal activity in the adrenal cortex (Sayers *et al.*, 1948), the results of these experiments indicate that sodium sulphide, in doses that cause excitation of the carotid chemoreceptors, increases adrenal cortical activity.

The experiments on decerebrate cats yielded similar results. The index of adrenal cortex activity in these experiments was reduction in the number of eosinophil cells in the peripheral blood. The decerebration by itself led to eosinopenia but special experiments revealed that the fall in the number of eosinophils had almost ceased 2 hr after the operation and their level then became more or less stable. Sodium sulphide was, therefore, injected 2 hr after decerebration and the eosinophil count before the injection was taken as the initial level. The sodium sulphide was injected intravenously in amounts of 10–15 mg/kg in freshly prepared solution, doses which produced appreciable dyspnoea in decerebrate cats. In all six experiments the injection of sodium sulphide led to reduction in the number of eosinophil cells in the blood, the count being about half the initial number 1 hr after the injection. In the controls, which were decerebrate but not given sulphide, the number of eosinophils was reduced by an average of only 3·7% after the same period.

An attempt was made to determine to what extent reflexes from the carotid bodies increased the activity of the adrenal cortex in decerebrate cats with the carotid sinuses denervated. The operation resulted in a reduction of the number of eosinophils in the peripheral blood, but the fall ceased after 2 hr and any increase of eosinopenia was very slow thereafter. The usual dose of sodium sulphide was injected intravenously 2 hr after the operation in experiments on four decerebrate cats with the sinuses denervated. Only in one of these experiments was the injection of sulphide followed by any appreciable increase of eosinopenia and in the other three experiments the reduction in the number of eosinophils in the peripheral blood of the cats was no greater than in the control animals.

These experiments provide evidence that reflexes from the carotid chemoreceptors play an important part in the increase of activity in the adrenal cortex after the administration of sulphide.

Roizhenkov also demonstrated the effect of sulphide-induced excitation of the carotid chemoreceptors on the secretion of the adrenal cortex in his experiments on unanaesthetized dogs. The 17-oxycorticosteroids in the blood were estimated directly in these experiments (Yudayev and Pankov's modification of Zil'ber and Porter's method, 1958). The intravenous injection of sodium sulphide (2·0–2·5 mg/kg, freshly prepared in 2% solution) resulted in a considerable increase of the 17-hydro-oxycorticosteroids in the peripheral blood of the dogs after 25–35 min.

When the same dose of sulphide was injected intravenously into a dog with the sinuses denervated the increase in the 17-oxycorticosteroid content of the blood was much less (an average of 16·2% as compared with 96·8% in dogs with normally innervated sinuses). The results of these experiments indicate the importance of the carotid chemoreceptors in the stimulation of the adrenal cortex produced by sulphides.

The increase in the content of corticosteroids in the blood of the dogs with the sinuses denervated was found to be statistically insignificant, but this may have depended on the small number of experiments. A participation of other chemoreceptors, and particularly the chemoreceptors in the aortic zones not excluded by denervation of the carotid sinuses, in the action of hypoxic poisons on the adrenal cortex must be considered.

That the function of the adrenal cortex was influenced by reflexes developing from the action of sulphides on the carotid bodies was also proved by Roizhenkov's experiments in which sulphide was injected into the carotid artery of unanaesthetized dogs.

TABLE 11

EFFECT OF SODIUM SULPHIDE ON THE ASCORBIC ACID CONTENT OF THE SUPRARENAL GLANDS OF RATS

| No. of experiment | Dose of sodium sulphide (mg/kg) | Time after injection (min) | Ascorbic acid (mg %) | | Change in ascorbic acid content | | Value of t $\dfrac{M - M_1}{\sqrt{m^2 - m_1^2}}$ required/obtained |
			Without sodium sulphide $M \pm m$	After injection of sodium sulphide $M_1 \pm m_1$	mg %	Percentage	
1	15	30	401·3	344·7	− 56·6	−14·1	
2	15	30	418·7	259·4	−159·3	−28·5	
3	20	30	388·7	351·4	− 37·3	− 9·6	
4	15	30	365·1	259·6	−105·5	−28·9	
5	20	30	432·5	374·6	− 57·9	−13·4	
Average			401·2 ± 12·9 $M \pm m$	317·9 ± 27·2 $M_1 \pm m_1$	− 83·3	−18·9	2·78/2·76
1	20	60	371·2	257·0	−114·2	−30·8	
2	15	60	400·6	302·5	− 98·1	−24·5	
3	20	60	384·4	324·1	60·3	−15·7	
4	15	60	422·4	284·7	−137·7	−32·6	
5	15	60	412·8	330·3	− 82·5	−20·0	

			$M \pm m$	$M_1 \pm m_1$			
Average			$398·3 \pm 10·4$	$299·7 \pm 14·9$	$-98·5$	$-24·7$	$2·78/5·3$
1	15	120	405·3	362·8	$-42·5$	$-10·5$	
2	20	120	442·7	353·3	$-89·4$	$-20·2$	
3	20	120	384·5	333·0	$-51·5$	$-13·4$	
4	15	120	360·2	284·6	$-75·6$	$-21·0$	
5	15	120	381·9	310·9	$-71·0$	$-18·6$	
Average			$394·9 \pm 15·5$	$328·9 \pm 15·8$	$-66·0$	$-16·6$	$2·78/2·98$
			$M \pm m$	$M_1 \pm m_1$			
1	15	240	362·7	306·9	$-55·8$	$-15·4$	
2	20	240	380·4	309·7	$-70·7$	$-18·6$	
3	20	240	415·6	330·0	$-85·6$	$-20·6$	
4	15	240	421·4	461·4	$+40·0$	$+9·5$	
5	15	240	390·1	336·3	$-53·8$	$-13·8$	
Average			$394·0 \pm 12·2$	$344·8 \pm 32·1$	$-61·1$	$-11·8$	$2·78/1·48$
			$M \pm m$	$M_1 \pm m_1$			

The isolated sinus method was used in these experiments. A preliminary operation was carried out in which the carotid artery was exteriorized in a skin flap and all the arterial branches in the region of the sinus with the exception of the arterioles supplying the carotid bodies and the lingual artery were ligatured.

The experiments were started after the operation wound had healed. When sodium sulphide was injected into the carotid artery of these dogs, the action of this rapidly-destroyed poison was virtually limited to the carotid body and the tongue muscles.

Sodium sulphide injected in this way increased the 17-oxycorticosteroid content both of the peripheral blood and the blood in the inferior vena cava, the latter collected by a polyethylene catheter introduced through the femoral vein. As a control, the same dose of sodium sulphide was injected into the carotid artery on the opposite side, on which the sinus had been denervated. Only a very slight increase of the 17-oxycorticosteroid content of the blood was observed to follow the injection of sulphide in these control experiments (Fig. 8).

The conclusion from all these experiments carried out by Roizhenkov is that the increase of adrenocortical secretion produced by sulphides is essentially the result of their stimulating effect on the carotid chemoreceptors.

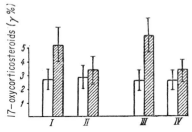

FIG. 8. Average 17-oxycorticosteroid content of the blood plasma in dogs before (blank columns) and after (shaded columns) action of sodium sulphide.
I—intravenous injection of sodium sulphide (2·0 mg/kg) to dogs with their carotid sinus zones intact. II—injection of saline to the same dogs. III—injection of sodium sulphide into the common carotid artery of dogs with the carotid sinus "isolated" (see text). IV—the same after the injection of sodium sulphide into the common carotid artery on the side of the denervated carotid sinus.

SODIUM AZIDE

Azides, particularly sodium azide (NaN_3), must be included along with cyanides and sulphides among the poisons fixing cytochromoxidase and thus inhibiting tissue respiration (Keilin, 1936). As the carotid chemoreceptors are highly sensitive to hydrocyanic acid and its salts and to hydrogen sulphide and sulphides, it was natural to expect that sodium azide would also have a powerful stimulating effect on chemoreceptors.

The effect of sodium azide on the carotid receptors has been demonstrated experimentally by Anichkov (1945). This work was carried out on dogs in acute experiments that gave evidence of the effect of azide on the carotid bodies. The animals were anaesthetized with Sombutal or a combination of Sombutal and urethane. Indication of activity on the carotid bodies was reflex respiratory excitation in the form of a sharp increase of amplitude and acceleration of the rate of the respiratory movements, lasting 2–3 min. Injection of the same dose of azide after preliminary denervation of the carotid sinuses produced practically no respiratory excitation.

These experiments had already proved the important part of the carotid chemoreceptors in the respiratory excitation produced by sodium azide. The direct stimulating effect of sodium azide on the carotid chemoreceptors was demonstrated in experiments in which the poison was injected into the arterial blood stream and into the stream of fluid perfusing the sinus. All the branches from one of the dog's carotid arteries in the region of the bifurcation, with the exception of the lingual artery and the small arteries supplying the carotid bodies, were dissected out and ligatured. Sodium azide solution (0·5 ml of 1 : 20,000–1 : 10,000) was injected through a cannula inserted into the central end of the superior thyroid artery on the side of operation. Injection was immediately followed by powerful respiratory excitation, undoubtedly the result of the action of azide on the carotid chemoreceptors, as it did not develop when the carotid sinus on the side of the injection had been denervated.

The stimulating effect of sodium azide was confirmed in experiments in which the carotid sinus was perfused. One of the dog's carotid sinuses was isolated by the Heymans method and perfused with ordinary Ringer–Locke solution. An intake cannula was inserted into the common carotid artery and the outflow cannula into the lingual artery. All the other arteries in the region of the bifurcation, with the exception of the small arteries supplying the carotid body, had been ligatured with the greatest possible care. The fluid to the sinus was delivered from a Mariotte vessel placed at a height of 180 cm. Sodium azide, 0·5 ml of a 0·2% solution, was injected with a syringe into the perfusion fluid. Powerful respiratory excitation was observed when azide was injected (Fig. 9).

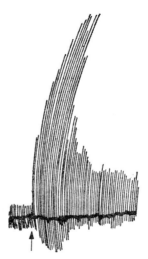

FIG. 9. Dog under Sombutal-urethane narcosis. Isolated carotid sinus. Recording of respiration. The arrow indicates the injection into the perfusing fluid of sodium azide (0·5 ml of 0·2% solution).

The stimulating effect of sodium azide on the carotid chemoreceptors has been confirmed by Dontas (1955). In these experiments oscillographic recordings were made from Hering's nerve in cats under chloralose and urethane anaesthesia, after an infection of 0·5 ml of sodium azide solution in concentrations of from 0·5 × 0·16 to 2 × 0·16 μM/ml into the carotid sinus through a polyethylene catheter inserted into the lingual artery.

Chemoreceptor excitation developed 6–8 sec after the azide injection and lasted for about 1 min. The chemoreceptors then remained insensitive to a further injection of sodium azide or sodium cyanide for several minutes.

When the reactions to azide and cyanide had been lost after the administration of small doses of azide, the reaction to acetylcholine still persisted. After the injection of large doses of sodium azide the chemoreceptors failed to react to both cyanide and acetylcholine.

All these investigations prove beyond doubt that sodium azide, like other poisons blocking cytochrome oxidase, has a powerful stimulating effect on the carotid chemoreceptors, an effect which is followed by depression.

CHAPTER II

Substances Affecting Cholinergic and Adrenergic Processes

ACETYLCHOLINE

Sensitivity of the Carotid Chemoreceptors to Acetylcholine and the Respiratory and Blood Pressure Reflexes produced by it

Powerful excitation of the carotid chemoreceptors produced by acetylcholine was demonstrated in experiments carried out in our laboratory in 1934, the results of which were submitted in 1935 to the 15th International Congress of Physiologists (see Anichkov et al., 1936).

At the same Congress Heymans et al. reported their experiments on the action of acetylcholine on the carotid bodies of the dog (1936).

Our experiments were carried out on the isolated sinus in decerebrate cats and have been described in detail in the candidate dissertation of Polyakov-Stanevich and in a paper by him (1938a).

When acetylcholine 10^{-7} was passed through the isolated sinus of the cat, there was development of acute respiratory excitation. When the acetylcholine perfusion was continued for 10 or 12 min, respiratory excitation was observed throughout that period. This respiratory stimulation was undoubtedly the result of a reflex from the carotid sinuses as it did not develop when acetylcholine was passed through the previously denervated or procaine treated sinus.

Experiments were designed to determine whether the chemoreceptors of the carotid bodies were the source of the reflexes produced by acetylcholine. The method employed by Heymans for the analysis of reflexes produced by other poisons was used. A suspension of lycopodium was injected into the isolated sinus to produce embolism of the arterioles supplying the carotid bodies. Thereafter, perfusion of the sinus with acetylcholine no longer led to respiratory excitation, although the baroreceptor reaction to compression of the carotid artery was unchanged (Polyakov-Stanevish, 1938b).

In Heymans' experiments on dogs a small amount of acetylcholine was injected into the blood perfusing the sinus. Each injection of acetylcholine was followed by dyspnoea of short duration, beginning with a single violent inspiration ("gasp") followed by rapid and deep respiration for several seconds. This effect was abolished by procaine infiltration of the sinus.

The carotid chemoreceptor excitation was particularly evident at the beginning of the application of acetylcholine. Perfusion of the isolated carotid sinus with acetylcholine, particularly with relatively strong concentrations, was continued for some time. The initial respiratory excitation was followed by a decline in the amplitude of the respiratory movement. Belen'kii, in his experiments on the effect of adenosine triphosphate on chemoreceptor sensitivity, perfused the isolated sinus with acetylcholine solution for a considerable time. Perfusion with acetylcholine 1:50,000 led to violent respiratory excitation lasting only 2–3 min, and when the perfusion was continued, respiration was depressed and eventually returned to its original depth or fell below it (Belen'kii, 1951b, 1951c, 1952a).

This respiratory depression, like the depression produced by prolonged perfusion of the sinus with cyanide, was abolished by the injection of adenosine triphosphate into the perfusion fluid.

Direct proof that the prolonged action of acetylcholine leads to decline of the excitability of the carotid chemoreceptors after the initial excitation can be obtained by sinus nerve oscillography. The action potentials developing in the sinus nerve as a result of the action of acetylcholine on the carotid sinus were first described by Euler *et al.* (1941). Experimenting on cats, they injected a small amount of acetylcholine into the external carotid artery towards the sinus. 5–10 γ-acetylcholine was sufficient to produce rapid potentials characteristic of impulses from chemoreceptors in the sinus nerve.

Potentials developing in the sinus nerve as a result of the action of acetylcholine on the carotid bodies can also be seen in the completely isolated sinus outside the body, that is when all indirect influence on the sinus can be excluded.

S. S. Krylov has shown that, when the completely isolated sinus is perfused with acetylcholine in concentrations of 1:10,000 and 1:5000, intense electrical activity develops in the sinus nerve in the form of large fast potentials, indicative of a stream of impulses reaching the nerve from chemoreceptors.

In Krylov's* experiments (personal communication) the injection of sodium cyanide into the perfusion fluid still produced a slight increase in the amplitude of the potentials in the sinus nerve after the chemoreceptors had been depressed by the prolonged passage of acetylcholine and had reached a state of insensitivity to acetylcholine.

When the stimulating effect of acetylcholine on the carotid chemoreceptors was first demonstrated, there was speculation as to the nature of the effects responsible for this action: was it a manifestation of the nicotine-like or muscarine-like effect of acetylcholine? The classification of the effects of acetylcholine into muscarine-like and nicotine-like, was suggested by Dale. He called the effect of acetylcholine at the level of the peripheral postganglionic synapses of the parasympathetic nerves, that is its action on cholinoreactive systems in the heart, vessels, glands and smooth muscle, muscarine-like. Muscarine has a selective action on these cholinergic systems.

Dale called the effect of acetylcholine at the level of the ganglionic synapses, of the cholinergic synapses in the suprarenal medulla and of the neuromuscular synapses of striated muscle the nicotine-like effect. Nicotine has a selective action on these synapses.

It must be assumed that the "different effect of acetylcholine" depends on differences in the sensitivities of cholinoreactive biochemical systems in different synapses.

We suggested, therefore, that cholinoreactive systems should be divided into two classes, namely muscarine-sensitive (M-cholinergic systems) and nicotine-sensitive (N-cholinergic systems) (Anichkov and Grebenkina, 1946; Anichkov, 1952).

The use of different acetylcholine antagonists is the best method for determining the nature of the effect of acetylcholine on the carotid bodies, whether they are muscarine-like or nicotine-like, or in other words, whether the cholinergic systems of the carotid bodies are M-cholinergic or N-cholinergic.

* *Fiziologicheskii Zh. SSSR*, **46**, 4, p. 429 (1960).

Even in very low concentrations, atropine is known to abolish all the muscarine-like effects of acetylcholine, whereas the nicotine-like effects are only suppressed by relatively high concentrations.

Polyakov-Stanevich (1938a) carried out experiments on the effect of combinations of acetylcholine and atropine on the isolated carotid sinuses of cats.

The isolated sinus was perfused with atropine in various concentrations, followed (usually after 5 min), by acetylcholine added to the perfusion fluid in a concentration (1:100,000) which would normally have a powerful effect. The index of carotid chemoreceptor reaction was respiratory stimulation. It was found that atropine in a concentration of 10^{-6}, which completely suppressed the effect of acetylcholine on the heart, the intestine and other organs in which its muscarine-like effects are seen, had no effect on the sensitivity of the carotid bodies for acetylcholine. These results were subsequently completely confirmed by other authors. Belous (1952) showed that the intravenous injection of acetylcholine into atropinized unanaesthetized dogs produced violent panting. This respiratory excitation was the result of reflexes from the carotid bodies, as it did not develop in dogs with the sinuses denervated. Atanackovic and Dalgaard-Mikkelsen (1951) demonstrated in experiments on anaesthetized dogs that atropinization, which completely abolished the hypotensive and other muscarine-like effects of acetylcholine, did not eliminate blood pressure reflexes produced by acetylcholine from the carotid bodies.

Thus, doses of atropine which block M-cholinergic systems throughout the body did not suppress the sensitivity of the carotid chemoreceptors for acetylcholine. It can, therefore, be concluded that the action of acetylcholine on the carotid chemoreceptors is a nicotine-like effect. In other words, the cholinoreactive systems of the carotid bodies are N-cholinoreactive.

Another weighty piece of evidence in favour of this conclusion is afforded by the very pronounced selective action of nicotine and closely related alkaloids on the carotid chemoreceptors.

This effect takes place in two stages (like the action of nicotine on other N-cholinoreactive systems), namely a stage of excitation and a subsequent stage of depression with disappearance of the reaction to acetylcholine.

F

When the isolated sinus of the cat was perfused with a comparatively strong nicotine solution (10^{-5}) there was initial vigorous respiratory excitation and then the breathing quietened down and the sinus became insensitive or almost insensitive to acetylcholine. The acute reduction of carotid body sensitivity to acetylcholine produced by the action of strong nicotine concentrations would point to a nicotine-like effect of acetylcholine on the carotid bodies. But Asratyan (1938b) has shown that strong concentrations of nicotine reduce the sensitivity of the carotid bodies for carbon dioxide and cyanide as well as for acetylcholine, although not to the same degree. The suppression of sensitivity to acetylcholine can, therefore, be regarded as part of a reduction of the general reactivity of chemoreceptors resulting from exceptionally fatiguing excitation. It is, therefore, very important to supplement the analysis by investigation with substances that block N-cholinoreactive systems without first exciting them. One such substance is D-tubocurarine. The various publications mentioned led Anichkov (1947) to make experiments with curare on the isolated carotid sinus. Experiments in which the isolated sinuses were perfused in dogs under Narkolan (bromethol) anaesthesia and in decerebrate cats showed that when the sinus was perfused with curare its sensitivity to acetylcholine disappeared or was very much reduced whereas sensitivity to cyanide was completely retained in a great majority of the experiments.

Similar results were then obtained with other cholinolytic substances that block N-cholinoreactive systems selectively. Such substances include the gangliolytics (salts of tetraethylammonium, hexamethonium, etc.) Suppression of the sensitivity of the carotid chemoreceptors to acetylcholine has been demonstrated in dogs by Moe *et al.* (1948) and in cats by Vedeneyeva (1951) in our laboratory.

A similar effect on the carotid chemoreceptors has been demonstrated in cats for hexamethylene-bis-trimethylammonium (hexamethonium) by Douglas (1952) and this has been confirmed in our laboratory by Denisenko (1958). All these authors have found that gangliolytic preparations suppress the sensitivity of the carotid bodies to acetylcholine in concentrations which have no or very little effect on their sensitivity to hypoxic poisons or, in other words, on their basic physiological function.

The position thus is that substances that block N-cholino-reactive systems and thus suppress the nicotine-like effects of acetylcholine also abolish its effect on the carotid chemoreceptors. This constitutes direct proof that the action of acetylcholine on the chemoreceptors in the carotid body is nicotine-like in character and, consequently, proof that they contain N-cholinoreactive systems.

Experiments on decerebrate cats (see Polyakov-Stanevich, 1938a) and on dogs under barbiturates (Heymans *et al.*, 1936) have shown that the action of acetylcholine on the carotid chemo-receptors leads to a rise of blood pressure at the same time as it stimulates respiration. This pressor effect is elicited by a reflex as it is not seen when acetylcholine acts on the denervated or procaine located sinus.

The reflex effect of acetylcholine on blood pressure is thus the opposite of the depressor of acetylcholine which is due to a direct action on vessels and heart.

It must be remembered that a reflex increase of pressure when acetylcholine passes through the isolated carotid sinus can only be seen when all the arterioles arising from the carotid artery are ligatured. Otherwise acetylcholine may escape into the general circulation and cause a fall of blood pressure.

Perfusion experiments on the isolated carotid sinus demonstrate convincingly that reflex stimulation of respiration and blood pressure occur as a result of the action of acetylcholine on the carotid chemoreceptors. But such experiments do not allow us to express an opinion to what extent these reflexes are concerned in the respiratory and blood pressure changes observed when acetylcholine is absorbed.

The violent panting seen in unanaesthetized dogs when acetylcholine is injected intravenously may possibly be ascribed to a baroreceptor reaction resulting from the sharp fall in blood pressure. The direct action of acetylcholine on the respiratory centre may also be involved in this dyspnoea.

Belous's experiments (1952, 1953) have shown, however, that reflexes from carotid chemoreceptors are mainly responsible for the dyspnoea which develops when acetylcholine is injected intravenously. These experiments were carried out on normal dogs without anaesthesia. The acetylcholine was injected intra-venously in doses of from 0·3 to 0·8 mg/kg. The dogs were given preliminary injections of atropine to prevent the blood pressure falling. Despite the atropinization and the absence of any depressor effect, acetylcholine caused the dogs to pant severely. This dyspnoea was the result of a reflex from the carotid bodies, as no respiratory excitation developed when the same doses of acetylcholine were injected into the same dogs after removal of the carotid bodies. (An aseptic technique was used for this operation which was only resumed when the wound had healed completely, experiments with acetylcholine were resumed exactly as before the operation.) The fundamental cause of the respiratory excitation in the stage of acetylcholine absorption was, therefore, its effect on the carotid chemoreceptors. The importance of carotid chemoreceptor reflexes in the effect of acetylcholine on blood pressure is less evident. These reflexes may to some extent minimize the catastrophic fall of blood pressure which is produced by the direct action of acetylcholine on the vessels and heart.

Experimental conditions can be produced in which the pressor effect of acetylcholine develops with full force. We know that when atropine is injected into an animal in a dose which blocks M-cholinoreactive systems completely, acetylcholine no longer produces a fall of blood pressure and larger doses actually produce a pressor effect. This effect is the result of the action of acetylcholine on N-cholinoreactive systems (nicotine-like action). It is usually thought that the main cause of this "inverse" pressor effect is the stimulating effect of acetylcholine on sympathetic ganglia and on the adrenal medulla. Atanackovic and Dalgaard-Mikkelsen (1951) have shown, however, that reflexes from chemoreceptors constitute the basis of the pressor effect of acetylcholine in atropinized animals. Their experiments were carried out on atropinized dogs under chloralose anaesthesia. It was noted that acetylcholine in doses sufficient to produce "inverse" pressor effects in atropinized dogs might even cause a certain fall of blood pressure after denervation of the carotid sinuses and bilateral vagotomy.

In experiments designed to determine whether the elimination of the "inverse" effect of acetylcholine associated with denervation of the sinuses was due to the hypertension that develops as a result of the operation, only the chemoreceptors of the carotid bodies were denervated and the baroreceptor innervation of the carotid sinus was left intact.

Initially, the blood pressure of these dogs was normal; yet, despite this, acetylcholine after atropinization produced not a pressor, but a slight depressor effect. Only considerably larger doses of acetylcholine led to increase of blood pressure after a preliminary fall in atropinized dogs with the chemoreceptor zones denervated. The cause of the increase of blood pressure in this case was apparently the direct action of acetylcholine on sympathetic ganglia and on the suprarenals. Unfortunately, the authors do not state the doses of acetylcholine used.

Neurohypophyseal Reflexes

The reflexes arising as the result of the action of acetylcholine on the carotid chemoreceptors are not limited to effects on respiration and blood pressure but are, like the reflex-responses to hypoxic poisons, much more widely distributed. Reflexes of this kind which attracted our attention were those involving the neurohypophysis.

It has previously been demonstrated (Pickford, 1939; Belous, 1948) that the arrest of water diuresis resulting from the intravenous injection of acetylcholine is due to increased postpituitary secretion, as no such arrest was seen in hypophysectomized dogs. Belous carried out experiments designed to determine whether reflexes from carotid chemoreceptors were concerned in this acetylcholine effect (Belous, 1953). Working with dogs, this author found that when acetylcholine in doses of from 0·4 to 0·8 mg/kg was injected intravenously and relatively rapidly (in the course of 5 sec), there was arrest of the diuresis resulting from water loading tests. This effect was not connected with the hypotensive effect of acetylcholine as the experiments were carried out on atropinized dogs.

Diuresis was arrested immediately after the injection of acetylcholine and the arrest lasted 30 min. The carotid sinuses were denervated and the carotid bodies removed in some of the experimental dogs. The experiments with water tests and acetylcholine injections were repeated on these dogs when the operation wounds had healed. In a great majority of these experiments doses of acetylcholine which, before denervation of the sinuses, produced pronounced arrest of water diuresis had no appreciable effect on diuresis after denervation, which meant that they did not increase the secretion of antidiuretic hormone ("vasopressin"). Slight arrest of diuresis was observed in only two cases. It would appear, therefore, that reflexes from carotid chemoreceptors play some part in the posterior pituitary hypersecretion caused by acetylcholine. When relatively small doses of acetylcholine were injected, these reflexes were of decisive importance in the antidiuretic effect.

When large doses of acetylcholine are injected the antidiuretic effect may be due to the direct action of acetylcholine on the hypothalamic region and hypophysis as well as to reflexes from the chemoreceptor zones. This becomes particularly probable when the stimulating effect of acetylcholine on the isolated hypophysis of the cat, demonstrated by Belous (1950), is considered.

ESTERS AND ETHERS
RELATED TO ACETYLCHOLINE

The discovery of the stimulating effect of acetylcholine on carotid chemoreceptors was immediately followed by investigations to determine the effect on the carotid chemoreceptors of esters structurally related to acetylcholine. Carbaminoylcholine (carbachol, doryl) has a powerful stimulating effect on the carotid bodies (Dautrebande and Marechal, 1933). It has selective action on both M-cholinergic and N-cholinergic systems, like acetylcholine, but unlike the latter, it is resistant to cholinesterase.

Comparatively large doses of acetyl-β-methylcholine and the ethyl ether of β-methylcholine were found to have stimulating effects on the carotid chemoreceptors (De Wispeleare, 1936, 1937). Phillipot (1937) carried out a systematic examination of the effects of choline derivatives on carotid chemoreceptors. This author states that his purpose was to investigate the hypothesis enunciated by Anichkov (1934, 1936) and Mercier et al. (1934a, 1934c) that all substances with nicotine-like actions stimulated carotid chemoreceptors. Phillipot carried out his experiments on dogs anaesthetized with chloralose. The test substances that had powerful actions were injected directly into the common carotid artery in concentrations of 1:1000, or 1:10,000. A preliminary intravenous injection of 2 mg atropine sulphate was given to prevent the very marked fall of blood pressure produced by choline esters. The index of the strength of the stimulating effect on the carotid chemoreceptors was the degree of reflex respiratory excitation. The reflex pressor effect was recorded simultaneously. In all, twenty-eight compounds including esters of choline and its alkyl derivatives, were tested.

The results of Phillipot's experiments are given in Table 12, which is borrowed from his paper. The author gives in the Table information on the muscarine-like and nicotine-like effects of the compounds tested; these are taken from the results obtained by various authors on other experimental material.

Table 12 shows that acetylcholine itself and carb-aminoyl-choline have the most powerful stimulating effects on the carotid cholino-receptors. In addition to their muscarine-like effects, these substances have in comparison with other compounds, powerful nicotine-like effects. After them, in strength of action on carotid receptors, come choline and simple choline ethers and esters such as acetylhomocholine (acetyl-γ-methylcholine).

All these substances have both muscarine-like and nicotine-like properties. Conversely, all the ethers and esters of β-methylcholine, which have powerful muscarine-like but no nicotine-like effects, had no action whatever on the carotid chemoreceptors under the same experimental conditions.

Phillipot's findings thus indicate that only choline derivatives which have nicotine-like effects possess a selective stimulating action on the carotid bodies; consequently, their influence on the carotid bodies may be regarded as one of the manifestations of the nicotine-like action of cholinomimetic substances.

The effects of some esters of choline and of β-methylcholine on the carotid bodies has also been studied by Liljestrand and Zotterman (1954) in experiments on cats anaesthetized with chloralose, or curarized and on artificial respiration. The test substances were injected into the carotid artery close to the carotid sinus. The reaction of the carotid bodies to the substance injected was recorded oscillographically from the sinus nerve. In addition to acetylcholine, the choline esters tested were propionylcholine, butyrylcholine and benzoylcholine. The first two were little inferior to acetylcholine in strength and, in doses of from 2 to 10 γ, produced a considerable but very transient burst of electrical

TABLE 12

COMPARATIVE ACTIVITIES OF CHOLINE ESTERS (PHILLIPOT, 1937)

Compound	Muscarine-like action	Nicotine-like action	No. of experimental dogs	No. of experiments on one animal	Dose (mg)	Carotid sinus effect on respiration
Choline	++	++	3	3	0·5–1·0	++
Acetylcholine	+++++	+++	7	2	0·01–0·1	++++
Carbaminoylcholine	+++	+++	8	3	0·01–0·1	++++
Methyl ether of choline	+++	++	3	2	0·025–0·1	+++++
Ethyl ether of choline	++	++	8	3	0·02–0·1	+++++
Butyl ether of choline	—	+++	6	2	0·01–1·0	+++++
Vinyl ether of choline	++	++	3	2	0·05–0·2	++
α-methylcholine	++	+	6	2	0·2–0·1	+
β-methylcholine	++		5	3	0·1–0·25	—
Acetyl-β-methylcholine	+++++	—	8	2	0·025–0·4	—
Carbaminoyl-β-methylcholine	+++++	—	8	4	0·01–0·4	—
Methyl ether of β-methyl-choline	+++		2	2	0·2	—
Ethyl ether of β-methyl-choline	+++++	—	6	3	0·05–0·4	—
Homocholine (γ-methyl-choline)	++	++	6	2	0·25–0·1	++
Acetylhomocholine	++	++	3	2	0·025–0·2	+++

β-ethylcholine	++	+	3	2	0·25–1·0	+
Acetyl-β-ethylcholine	++	±	3	2	0·25	−
Methyl ether of β-ethyl-choline	++	−	2	2	0·2	−
Ethyl ether of β-ethylcholine	+++	−	4	3	0·2–0·1	±
Butyl ether of β-ethylcholine	−	−	2	2	0·25	−
β-propylcholine		−	3	2	0·25–1·0	+
Acetyl-β-propylcholine	++	−	5	3	0·2–1·0	+
Methyl ether of β-propyl-choline	+	−	2	2	0·2	−
Ethyl ether of β-propyl-choline	++	−	4	3	0·2–0·23	±
Amyl ether of β-propyl-choline	−	−	3	2	0·2–0·25	−
β-butylcholine		−	3	2	0·1–1·0	+
Ethyl ether of β-butylcholine	−	−	2	3	0·2	−
Butyl ether of β-butylcholine	−	−	4	2	0·2–0·25	±

activity in the sinus nerves. The action of butyrylcholine was slightly weaker than that of proprionylcholine in most experiments. Benzoylcholine was much inferior to these in strength of action and had to be injected in larger doses (five to ten times greater) to produce a stimulating effect.

The effect of acetyl-β-methylcholine on the carotid bodies was also very much weaker. On the other hand, the thio analogues of acetylcholine and butyrylcholine tested by these authors had powerful and relatively prolonged effects. Choline esters are known to lose their muscarine-like properties, while retaining intense nicotine-like action when the oxygen in choline is replaced by sulphur (see Bovet and Bovet-Nitti, 1948).

The results obtained by the Swedish authors by means of sinus nerve oscillography thus confirmed completely that the stimulating effects of esters of choline and its immediate derivatives are connected with their nicotine-like action. Findings obtained with other cholinomimetic substances on the carotid chemoreceptors lead to the same conclusion. In his experiments on decerebrate cats Polyakov-Stanevich (1938a) found that pilocarpine, which has an exclusively muscarine-action, had practically no effect on chemoreceptors when perfused through the isolated sinus in a strength of 1:100,000. He also found that arecoline 1:100,000 produced reflex respiratory excitation when perfused through the isolated sinus of the cat. In this strength arecoline has, in addition to its muscarine-like action, a stimulating effect on N-cholinoreactive systems.

The esters with dicarboxylic acids constitute a special group of choline derivatives. The general formula of these esters may be presented in the following form:

$$(CH_3)_3\overset{+}{N}CH_2CH_2O-\overset{\overset{\displaystyle O}{\|}}{C}-(CH_2)_n-\overset{\overset{\displaystyle O}{\|}}{C}.OCH_2CH_2\overset{+}{N}(CH_3)_3.(2x^-)$$

Such esters are sometimes called "diacetylcholines" as they can be regarded as two molecules of acetylcholine connected by a "polymethylene bridge". The attention of pharmacologists was primarily attracted by the curare-like properties of these compounds. These are very pronounced in the dicholine ester of succinic acid, succinylcholine (Bovet *et al.*, 1949, 1951).

Succinylcholine, like other diacetylcholines, differs sharply from D-tubocurarine in the mechanism of the curarizing effect. It produces paralysis of the postsynaptic structures in neuromuscular synapses through prolonged depolarization. This paralysis is preceded by fleeting excitation of the muscle fibres. Mikhel'son and his co-workers (Vishnyakov et al., 1952) have shown that a characteristic feature of the diacetylcholines is their selective stimulating effect on N-cholinoreactive systems in autonomic ganglia and the suprarenal glands. At the same time they are practically devoid of action on M-cholinoreactive systems.

As the cholinoreactive systems of the carotid bodies are sensitive to substances with nicotine-like actions, it was natural to expect that diacetylcholines would have a selective action on these carotid bodies.

The esters of this series do, in fact, in the stage of absorption, produce respiratory excitation caused by reflexes from the carotid chemoreceptors. Comparative studies of the reactions of this group revealed that the intensity of the stimulating effect of the diacetylcholines on the carotid chemoreceptors depended on the length of the polymethylene bridge connecting the choline groups.

Mikhel'son suggested that the dicholine esters of fatty acids should be labelled D_0, D_1, D_2, D_3, D_4 and so on, in accordance with the number of polymethylene groups in the bridge.

The stimulating effect of diacetylcholines on the carotid bodies increases with increase in the length of the polymethylene bridge from D_0 to D_6, that is, progressively from the ester of oxalic acid to that of suberic acid, the acid with 6 methylene groups, and then declines slightly with further lengthening of the bridge, as in the esters of adipic (4 methylene groups) and sebacic (8 methylene groups) acids. The stimulating effect of the diacetylcholines on autonomic ganglia and the suprarenal glands changes in the same order. On the carotid chemoreceptors they have been studied in Mikhel'son's laboratory by Vishnyakov (1952) in perfusion experiments on isolated carotid sinuses. It was found that even very small doses of dicholine esters had an action on cholinoreactive systems in the carotid bodies and that the esters which had the most powerful action on N-cholinoreactive systems in autonomic ganglia (e.g. esters of suberic and sebacic acids), when injected into the fluid passing through the isolated sinus, produced reflex respiratory excitation similar in intensity and duration to that produced by an equal dose of acetylcholine.

On the basis of their experiments on animals and of observations on human subjects, the group directed by Mikhel'son suggested the di-iodide of the dicholine ester of suberic (octanedioic) acid (which they called "Corconium") as a respiratory analeptic to replace lobeline and Cytitone (0–15% cytisine solution). (Dardymov and Rybolovlev, 1955; Mikhel'son et al., 1957.)

In the opinion of these authors, an important advantage of Corconium as a respiratory analeptic is its wide therapeutic activity. It can be used not only intravenously but also intramuscularly or subcutaneously, routes by which relatively large doses of respiratory analeptics with reflex action must be given in order to obtain respiratory effects.

The relatively low toxicity of Corconium, which is the basis of its wide therapeutic activity, is, in the opinion of the authors who recommend it, due to its feeble action on the central nervous system. The relatively weaker action of Corconium and other diacetylcholines on the central nervous system in comparison with lobeline, cytisine and other alkaloids of the nicotine group is linked with the fact that these di-esters, unlike the alkaloids named, are quaternary ammonium bases. The low toxicity of dicholine esters is also explained by the fact that, like acetylcholine, they are hydrolysed by cholinesterase. When diacetylcholines, including Corconium, are injected repeatedly they continue to stimulate respiration without toxic or side effects. According to observations made in Mikhel'son's laboratory (Mikhel'son et al., 1957; Dardymov and Rybolovlev, 1955), the subcutaneous injection of Corconium 0·5–0·8 mg/kg (0·3–0·5 ml of 10% solution) has a powerful stimulating effect on respiration lasting about 20 min in adult man. At the height of action the respiratory volume reached 20–45 l./min and the blood pressure rose by 20–50 mm Hg; no subjective or objective side effects were observed.

Rybolovlev (1957) describes certain findings on the connexion between the structure and effects of diacetylcholines and related compounds. Among the latter he examined the monocholine esters of higher homologues of dicarboxylic acids. He found that these monoesters have powerful nicotine-like actions which include respiratory stimulation. The author used this as a measure of their effect on the carotid chemoreceptors (Table 13).

Unlike that of dicholine esters, the nicotine-like activity of monocholine esters did not depend on the number of carbon

TABLE 13

NICOTINOMIMETIC ACTIVITIES OF MONOCHOLINE AND DICHOLINE ESTERS OF THE HIGHER HOMOLOGUES OF DICARBOXYLIC ACIDS (RYBOLOVLEV, 1957)

$$R-O-\overset{\overset{O}{\|}}{C}-(CH_2)_n-\overset{\overset{O}{\|}}{C}-CH_2-CH_2\overset{+}{N}\equiv(CH_3)_3 \quad J^-$$

Acid n	R	Doses giving equal effects (mg/kg)	
		Pressor effect	Respiratory excitation
Pimelic acid 5	$(CH_3)_3\equiv\overset{+}{N}-\overset{J^-}{C}H_2-CH_2$	0·005	0·03
Pimelic acid 5	$H-CH_2-CH_2-$	0·005	0·04
Suberic acid 6	$(CH_3)_3\equiv\overset{+}{N}-CH_2-\overset{J^-}{C}H_2-$	0·002	0·005
Suberic acid 6	$H-CH_2-CH_2-$	0·005	0·04
Azelaic acid 7	$(CH_3)_3\equiv\overset{+}{N}-\overset{J^-}{C}H_2-CH_2$	0·004	0·02
Azelaic acid 7	$H-CH_2-CH_2-$	0·005	0·04
Sebacic acid 8	$(CH_3)_3\equiv\overset{+}{N}-\overset{J^-}{C}H_2-CH_2-$	0·005	0·04
Sebacic acid 8	$H-CH_2-CH_2-$	0·005	0·04

atoms in the acid part of the molecule and was exactly the same in the esters of all dicarboxylic acids, including sebacic. The ester of the latter was equal in nicotinomimetic activity to its dicholine ester but inferior to the dicholine ester of azelaic and, more particularly, suberic acid. The presence of a second ammonium group thus increased the activity of the esters of azelaic and suberic acids, but not of all dicarboxylic acids. The changes in the activities of dicholine esters produced by replacement of the methyl by ethyl radicals was also investigated in this study. This substitution reduced nicotinomimetic activity considerably. When one methyl radical in each ammonium group of the dicholine ester of sebacic acid was replaced by an ethyl group, the respiratory stimulation was reduced to one-fortieth of its former intensity.

Bovet et al. (1949, 1951) have shown that dicholine esters have a paralysing effect on neuromuscular synapses. This curarizing effect is, however, very much weaker with the dicholine esters of suberic acid (Corconium) and sebacic acid than in the dicholine ester of succinic acid and is not seen at all with therapeutic doses that produce powerful respiratory excitation.

Mikhel'son's laboratory (Vishnyakov et al., 1952) has shown that succinylcholine also has a certain stimulating effect on carotid chemoreceptors but the curarizing effect which develops in the absorption stage of succinylcholine action prevents the development of respiratory excitation.

That succinylcholine excites the carotid chemoreceptors has also been demonstrated by Swedish authors in the laboratory of Prof. Liljestrand (Landgren et al., 1952) in experiments in which oscillographic recordings were made from the sinus nerve when succinylcholine was injected into a carotid artery.

QUATERNARY AMMONIUM BASES

Quaternary ammonium bases with the general formula

$$R^{I}-\underset{\underset{R^{IV}}{|}}{\overset{\overset{R^{II}}{|}}{N}}-R^{III} \ (x^-)$$

can be represented as ammonium, all the hydrogens of which have been replaced by hydrocarbon radicals. The simplest compound of this series is tetramethylammonium $\overset{+}{N}(CH_3)_4$, (x^-). Replacement of the hydrogen atoms in tetramethylammonium by various radicals yields a large series of compounds which are classed as quaternary ammonium bases. But only those which, like tetramethylammonium and its homologues, contain no other functional groups than the ammonium groups constitute a homogeneous group with similar basic pharmocological properties. This chapter deals mainly with these quaternary ammonium bases.

The characteristic pharmacological feature of these bases is their selective action on the N-cholinoreactive systems in both ganglia and skeletal muscles. It might, therefore, be expected that such compounds would also have selective action on the N-cholinoreactive systems of the carotid chemoreceptors. This has now been completely confirmed experimentally.

TETRAMETHYLAMMONIUM

It has long been known (see Trendelenburg, 1923) that tetramethylammonium (TMA) salts have a nicotine-like action on ganglia and suprarenal glands, the intensity of which is very similar to that of nicotine itself. Their first excitatory and then paralyzing effect on respiration has also been noted and this has been interpreted as the effect of the action of the poison on the respiratory centre, supplemented later by curare-like action. Yet, as tetramethylammonium possesses nicotine-like properties it can be postulated that the stimulating effect of this substance on respiration is in all probability the result of reflexes from carotid chemoreceptors.

The stimulating effect of tetramethylammonium on the carotid bodies has been demonstrated in our laboratory by Asratyan (1938a). This led to an investigation on the effect of quaternary ammonium bases on chemoreceptors.

These experiments were carried out on decerebrate cats. When TMA 0·002–0·01 mg/kg was injected into a femoral vein, respiration was powerfully stimulated. This did not occur or was seen only in very feeble form when reflexes from the sinuses had previously been excluded by the injection of 1% procaine solution into the surrounding cellular tissue. Another series of experiments was carried out on decerebrate cats with the carotid sinuses removed and the vagus nerves divided in the neck, in other words, with the main vascular reflexogenic zones excluded. The intravenous injection of TMA solution then led to respiratory depression, only sometimes preceded by slight excitation. The respiratory depression was particularly marked when comparatively large doses of TMA (50 γ/kg) were injected. It follows, therefore, that the direct effect of tetramethylammonium on the respiratory centre is predominantly one of depression.

The great sensitivity of the carotid bodies to TMA became particularly evident in experiments in which the isolated sinus was perfused in decerebrate cats in the standard manner adopted in our laboratory. Reflex respiratory excitation was observed in the cats when the sinus was perfused with TMA solutions in concentrations of even 10^{-7}.

This effect was very intense with concentrations of 1:500,000 and 1:100,000. It was not, however, observed at all after preliminary procaine treatment of the sinus. Comparing the effect of TMA with that of other poisons having nicotine-like properties, Asratyan found that TMA was superior to most of them in the intensity of its stimulant effect on the carotid chemoreceptors. When the various substances were perfused through the isolated sinus of the decerebrate cat the minimum active concentration of cytisine was found to be 1:2,000,000, that of TMA 1:1,000,000 and the minimum effective concentration of nicotine itself 1:2,000,000. Other alkaloids of the same group—lobeline, anabasine, coniine and sparteine—were found to have even weaker effects on the carotid chemoreceptors than TMA.

The results obtained by comparing the minimum concentrations that stimulate the carotid bodies have been confirmed by comparing the intensities of the respiratory excitation produced by passing these substances in equal concentrations through the isolated carotid sinus. TMA was again found to be more active than nicotine and all the other alkaloids tested with the exception of cytisine. When strong solutions of TMA (1:1,000,000 or more) were perfused through the isolated sinus, the initial excitation was followed by blockade of the N-cholinoreactive systems in the carotid bodies and they became insensitive to nicotine and acetylcholine.

TETRAETHYLAMMONIUM

Replacement of the methyl radicals of tetramethylammonium by ethyl radicals has a material effect on the pharmocological properties of the compound. Study of the properties of tetraethylammonium (TEA) (Burn and Dale, 1915; Hunt, 1926) has revealed the following differences from tetramethylammonium: (1) tetraethylammonium has much lower pharmacological activity and toxicity; (2) it has a blocking and not a stimulating effect on ganglia; (3) its stimulating effect at neuromuscular synapses is relatively greater (see Borodkin et al., 1958). As a result of the work of Acheson and his colleagues (Acheson and Moe, 1945; Acheson and Pereira, 1946; and others), the ability of tetraethylammonium to block ganglionic synapses has been extensively used in clinical work.

The first investigations on the effect of TEA on the carotid bodies, published in 1948, reported contradictory results. Moe et al. (1948) found that, in dogs, continuous intravenous infusion of TEA depressed the sensitivity of carotid chemoreceptors to acetylcholine and lobeline but had little effect on sensitivity to hypoxia and cyanides. On the other hand, Boelaert (1948), who carried out investigations in Heymans' laboratory, denied that TEA had any action on the carotid bodies.

Vedeneyeva (1951) carried out a systematic investigation of the effect of TEA on the carotid chemoreceptors in our laboratory. Our usual method—perfusion of the isolated sinus *in situ* in the cat, was used. Solutions of tetraethylammonium iodide in dilutions of 1:20,000 to 1:3000 were passed through the isolated sinus and the sensitivity of the carotid bodies was then tested with acetylcholine (1:3000–1:10,000), carbaminoylcholine (1:10,000–1:20,000), nicotine (1:5000–1:20,000) and also potassium cyanide (1:3000–1:5000). Solutions of all these poisons were injected into the perfusion fluid in quantities of 0·2–0·4 ml, the rate of perfusion being 2–2·5 ml/min. The experiments were carried out on twenty-five cats. When these poisons acted on the carotid bodies in the normal state, that is when perfusion was with pure Ringer–Locke solution, marked respiratory excitation was observed to result from excitation of the carotid chemoreceptors. In some of the acetylcholine experiments there was leakage from

G

the isolated sinus into the general circulation, which led to a fall of blood pressure and additional respiratory stimulation as a reaction from baroreceptors. To avoid this complication atropine was injected intravenously before the acetylcholine experiments. TEA in strength of 1:20,000 produced no changes in the chemical sensitivity of the carotid bodies but concentrations of 1:10,000 or more abolished the sensitivity of the carotid bodies to acetylcholine, carbaminoylcholine and nicotine in a great majority of experiments and the sensitivity was considerably reduced in the remaining ones. At the same time the reaction to cyanide was completely preserved. On the evidence of these experiments, TEA blocks the N-cholinoreactive systems of the carotid bodies selectively, without disturbing their sensitivity to hypoxia.

The N-cholinoreactive systems became blocked after the sinus has been perfused with TEA solutions for 3–10 min and the effect passed off after the sinus had been washed with pure Ringer–Locke solution for 5–10 min. Recording of the cat's respiration during perfusion of the isolated sinus with TEA solutions revealed that there was transient stimulation of respiration at the very commencement of TEA action in many cases. Respiratory stimulation was also occasionally observed when small quantities of TEA (0·2–0·4 ml of 1% solution) were injected into the perfusion fluid. As there was then no fall of blood pressure, the respiratory stimulation observed could not be ascribed to escape of TEA into the general circulation, with the production of hypotension.

The depression of carotid chemoreceptor excitability produced by TEA was, therefore, preceded by slight stimulation of these receptors.

The initial stimulant effect of TEA on the carotid bodies and the subsequent blockade point to some degree of similarity in the actions of tetramethylammonium and tetraethylammonium. The important pharmacological difference between these chemically closely related substances is, however, that, with tetramethylammonium, the initial stimulating effect on the carotid bodies is predominant whereas the subsequent blocking effect is very much more marked with tetraethylammonium. It should be emphasized that these substances differ in the same way in their action on ganglia whereas the reverse relationship holds for the neuromuscular synapses. These comparative considerations indicate that the N-cholinoreactive system of the carotid bodies are nearer to the corresponding system in autonomic ganglia than to that in skeletal muscle.

Liljestrand *et al.* (1952) made oscillographic recordings from the sinus nerve in their investigation of the effect of TEA on the carotid chemoreceptors. In their experiments the intravenous injection of 100 mg tetraethylammonium chloride led to considerable reduction in the amplitude and duration of the electrical discharges in the sinus nerve of the cat in response to the intracarotid injection of lobeline (1 mg) and acetylcholine (20 γ), although the reaction to oxygen lack in the inspired air was essentially unchanged. When 100 mg TEA was injected into the carotid artery during a period of great electrical activity in the sinus nerve produced by the breathing of a mixture poor in oxygen (5·2% O_2 in N_2), this activity was suppressed for a period of not less than 14 sec.

The Swedish authors concluded from their experiments that the actions of acetylcholine and lobeline on the carotid chemoreceptors were readily abolished by tetraethylammonium without a comparable reduction in the chemoreceptor sensitivity to oxygen lack. Yet, a certain reduction in the reaction to oxygen lack does occur as a result of the action of TEA and there is, therefore, only a quantitative difference between the effect of TEA on the sensitivity of the carotid bodies to lobeline and acetylcholine and their sensitivity to hypoxia.

HEXAMETHONIUM

The transition from N-cholinomimetics (e.g. trimethylammonium) to N-cholinolytics can be brought about not only by a substitution of ethyl for a methyl group but also by "reduplication" of the molecules. Such compounds are, as it were, two molecules of tetramethylammonium connected by a polymethylene bridge; they are called polymethylene-bis-trimethylammonium bases

$$(CH_3)_3\overset{+}{N}(CH_2)_n\overset{+}{N}(CH_3)_3 \cdot (2x^-)$$

Their salts have selective blocking actions on N-cholinergic systems. Comparative pharmacological examination of compounds of this series has shown that their predominant actions on different synapses depend on the length of the polymethylene chain (Paton and Zaimis, 1948, 1949). When the chain consists of five or six carbon atoms (pentamethonium and hexamethonium), gangliolytic action predominates; when there are ten carbon atoms in the chain (decamethonium), the compound has a selective blocking action on neuromuscular synapses.

The blocking effect of hexamethonium on carotid chemoreceptors was first demonstrated by Douglas (1952c). His experiments on cats showed that hexamethonium abolished the respiratory stimulation produced by acetylcholine, lobeline or nicotine but had no effect on dyspnoea caused by oxygen deficiency.

The direct action of hexamethylene-bis-trimethylammonium iodide (hexamethonium) on the carotid bodies has been investigated in our laboratory by Denisenko (1958).

The experiments were carried out on decerebrate cats, the isolated sinus being perfused and respiration recorded. The excitability of the carotid chemoreceptors was tested by the injecting into the perfusing fluid acetylcholine (1:5000), carbaminoylcholine (1:5000), nicotine (1:10,000), cytisine (1:5000) and potassium cyanide (1:5000). These solutions were injected in quantities of 0·5 ml, at a perfusion rate of 2–3 ml/min.

The effect of hexamethonium (1:100,000 and 1:75,000) was tested by perfusion through the sinus and also by injecting 1 ml of a 1% solution into the Ringer–Locke fluid. No very significant change in respiration was observed when hexamethonium acted on the isolated sinus; there was merely slight acceleration of the respiratory rate. It did, however, considerably reduce the chemical sensitivity of the cholinoreactive systems in the carotid bodies. The reactions of the chemoreceptors to acetylcholine, carbaminoylcholine, nicotine and cytisine were much reduced during hexamethonium perfusion and for some time after injection of hexamethonium into the perfusion fluid; there was, however, no change whatever in sensitivity to potassium cyanide. The block of the N-cholinoreactive systems in the carotid bodies by hexamethonium was reversible and, after washing of the sinus with pure Ringer–Locke solution for a sufficient period of time, sensitivity to acetylcholine, carbaminoylcholine, nicotine and cytisine was completely restored.

The gangliolytic substance, hexamethonium, like TEA, thus has a selective depressing action on the sensitivity of the carotid chemoreceptors to acetylcholine, nicotine and other N-cholino-mimetics, but is without effect on sensitivity to hypoxia and hypoxic poisons.

According to Byck's experiments (1961), hexamethonium in doses can produce a considerable reduction of carotid chemo-receptor sensitivity for nicotine and may even intensify the sensitivity to cyanide.

D-TUBOCURARINE. PARAMION

The effect of curare-like substances on the carotid chemo-receptors was first studied by Anichkov (1947). Curare (Merck), 0·6 mg of which immobilized a frog of average weight, was used in the experiments. The experiments were carried out on twenty dogs with a carotid sinus isolated according to Heymans. The dogs were under Sombutal anaesthesia (25–30 mg/kg intra-venously). Ringer–Locke fluid under pressure of 160–180 cm H_2O was passed through the sinus isolated on one side. A final curare concentration of 1:16,000 to 1:25,000 was present in the perfusion fluid.

In a great majority of the experiments the passage of curare solutions through the isolated sinus had no appreciable effect on respiration. In order to determine whether there was any change in the excitability of the chemoreceptors, poisons that produced reflex respiratory excitation through action on the carotid bodies were injected into the perfusion fluid. The substances used were nicotine, anabasine, carbaminoylcholine, potassium cyanide and sodium azide.

Nicotine, 0·5 ml of a 1:25,000 solution, injected into the rubber tubing carrying the perfusion fluid to the isolated sinus, normally produced vigorous respiratory stimulation. During perfusion with curare the sensitivity of the carotid chemoreceptors for nicotine disappeared and they failed to react not only to a nicotine in a concentration of 1:25,000 but to one of 1:5000. Loss of caro-tid chemoreceptor senstivity for nicotine was seen in all sixteen experiments. Curare abolished the response of the carotid bodies to anabasine (1:10,000) and carbaminoylcholine (1:10,000), substances which normally produced marked reflex respiratory excitation (Fig. 10). Washing the curarized sinus with pure Ringer–Locke solution for a quite considerable period restored the sensitivity of the chemoreceptors for nicotine, anabasine and carbaminoylcholine.

The effect of curare on the sensitivity of the carotid bodies for acetylcholine was also investigated. Acetylcholine, 0·5 ml of a 1:5000 solution, normally produced vigorous respiratory stimulation but, when the sinus had been perfused with curare, it

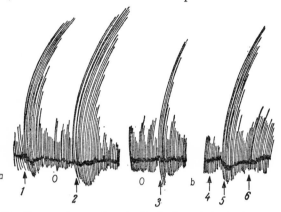

FIG. 10. Dog under sombutal. Perfusion of the isolated carotid sinus. Recording of respiration.
a—before, and b—3 min after the commencement of perfusion with curare (1/5000). Injection into the perfusing fluid of 0·5 ml: 1—potassium cyanide (1/5000). 2—anabasine (1/10,000). 3—carbocholine (1/10,000). 4—carbocholine (1/10,000). 5—potassium cyanide (1/5000). 6—anabasine (1/10,000). The drum was revolving at the rate of 1·5 cm/min. The drum was stopped for 5 min at 0.

gave no reaction whatever in two of the three experiments and in one the reaction was very much weaker than the normal reaction.

The antagonism of curare to acetylcholine was very much less pronounced when the latter was combined with physostigmine. A mixture of acetylcholine 1:25,000 and physostigmine 1:50,000 was used in these experiments, its effect being tested before and during perfusion with curare 1:5000. When 0·5 ml of this mixture was injected into the Ringer–Locke perfusion fluid acute respiratory stimulation was seen. When the sinus was perfused with curare the reaction to acetylcholine in combination with physostigmine was completely absent in only one of the three experiments, in another the reaction was slightly reduced after 6 min and markedly reduced but not completely absent after 14 min, and in the third experiment the reaction remained completely unchanged although the curare perfusion continued for 17 min.

It can be concluded from these experiments that curare reduces the sensitivity of the carotid bodies to ganglionic poisons and to acetylcholine, the effect being most pronounced for nicotine and weakest for the mixture of acetylcholine and physostigmine.

These experiments thus revealed a similarity between the effects of curare on the carotid bodies and on ganglia, in agreement with the findings on other ganglionic poisons. Curare blocks the carotid chemoreceptors sensitive to nicotine and acetylcholine just as it blocks the corresponding ganglionic N-cholinoreactive systems.

The ability of physostigmine, which preserves acetylcholine, to prevent the antagonistic action of curare for acetylcholine in the carotid bodies is analogous to the well-known property of physostigmine to abolish paralysis of striated muscle produced by curare.

The effect of curare on the excitability of the carotid chemoreceptors was tested with potassium cyanide and sodium azide as well as ganglionic poisons.

These experiments were carried out on the isolated sinuses of 11 dogs. Potassium cyanide was used in dilutions of 1:1000, 1:5000 and 1:10,000, and sodium azide in a dilution of 1:5000; these solutions were injected into the perfusion fluid in volumes of 0·5–1·0 ml, amounts which normally produced active reflex respiratory stimulation. It was found that potassium cyanide and sodium azide continued to exert their usual stimulating effect when perfusion was carried on in the presence of 1:2500–1:10,000 curare. In only two of the eleven experiments did potassium cyanide produce less respiratory excitation during the curare perfusion than before. It was impossible to exclude the entry of curare into the general circulation in these experiments.

In the remaining nine experiments potassium cyanide and sodium azide had, during the period of curare perfusion, the same reflex effect on respiration as they normally had, and sometimes the effect was even more marked although the sensitivity of the carotid bodies to nicotine and anabasine was at that time completely lost.

Curare, therefore, blocks the reactive systems in the carotid bodies to nicotine and acetylcholine, but it does not block the sensitivity of chemoreceptors to poisons that paralyse tissue respiration.

The effect of pure D-tubocurarine on carotid chemoreceptors has been studied in Liljestrand's laboratory (Landgren et al., 1952) in experiments on cats anaesthetized with chloralose. Carotid chemoreceptor excitation was assessed from oscillographic recordings from the sinus nerve. The reactions of the chemoreceptors to oxygen deficiency (breathing of a mixture containing 5·6% O_2) and to the injection of lobeline 300 γ into the carotid artery were tested. These normally produced great electrical activity in the sinus nerve.

D-Tubocurarine was injected into the carotid artery in doses ranging from 100 γ to 3 mg, dissolved in distilled water. The injection of even small doses of D-tubocurarine abolished the sensitivity of the chemoreceptors to lobeline completely for a certain period of time. To a certain extent, D-tubocurarine also suppressed chemoreceptor sensitivity to oxygen lack. Considerably larger doses of D-tubocurarine (1·5–3 mg) had, however, to be used to produce this effect; normal sensitivity to hypoxia returned 15–17 sec after the end of the D-tubocurarine injection—much earlier than restoration of sensitivity to lobeline.

The Swedish authors' experiments thus indicated that D-tubocurarine reduced all forms of chemical sensitivity in the carotid bodies and any difference in the effect of curarine on the sensitivity of the carotid chemoreceptors to lobeline and oxygen deficiency respectively was purely quantitative and not qualitative.

In the same investigation the Swedish authors tested the effect of a synthetic curare-like preparation, decamethonium, on the carotid chemoreceptors. Decamethonium iodide (2 mg) was injected into the common carotid artery, the latter being compressed; this had the effect of slowing the blood-flow and intensifying the action of the curare. Decamethonium injected when an oxygen-poor gaseous mixture was breathed, suppressed the electrical activity in the sinus nerve produced by the hypoxaemia.

The activity was completely suppressed for about 50 sec, but reached its normal limit again about 5 min after the decamethonium injection.

Decamethonium thus suppressed carotid chemoreceptor sensitivity to oxygen lack to a greater extent than D-tubocurarine. It may be mentioned in this connexion that decamethonium differs materially from D-tubocurarine in its mechanism of action, being a depolarizing agent and not a blocking agent.

The effect of a Soviet synthetic curare-like preparation, Paramion, on the carotid chemoreceptors has been studied in our laboratory by Mitrofanov (1957). Paramion (meso-3,4-diphenyl hexane n,n'-bis-trimethylammonium iodide) is closer in its mechanism of action to D-tubocurarine than to decamethonium (see Anichkov and Khromov-Borisov, 1958).

These experiments were carried out on decerebrate cats by our usual method of perfusing the isolated sinus. Paramion was used for perfusion in dilutions of from 1:5000 to 1:10,000.

Acetylcholine (0·4 ml of 1:25,000 solution) and sodium cyanide (0·2 ml of 1:1000 solution) were injected into the perfusion fluid to test the chemical sensitivity of the sinus.

After 1–3 min of perfusion with Paramion, which by itself produced no changes in respiration, the sensitivity of the carotid bodies to acetylcholine disappeared and acetylcholine injection into the perfusion fluid ceased to produce respiratory excitation. When the sinus was then perfused with pure Ringer–Locke solution, the sensitivity of the chemoreceptors for acetylcholine began to return after about 3 min.

Paramion solutions of the same strength (1:5000, 1:10,000) did not reduce the sensitivity of the carotid chemoreceptors to sodium cyanide.

To sum up available information on the effects of curare-like substances on the carotid chemoreceptors, it can be stated that all authors are agreed that these substances suppress chemoreceptor sensitivity to acetylcholine and to N-cholinomimetic substances selectively; in other words, curare-like substances block the N-cholinoreactive systems in the carotid bodies. Different authors express different views, however, on the effect of curare-like substances on the sensitivity of the carotid bodies to hypoxia. Soviet authors, who have generally perfused the isolated sinus and have employed respiratory excitation as the index of the reaction in testing the sensitivity of the chemoreceptors to cyanide, have not found that curare-like substances alter the sensitivity of chemoreceptors to hypoxia. The Swedish authors, however, brought curare-like substances to act on the chemoreceptors by injecting them into the blood in the carotid artery during the breathing of an oxygen-poor gaseous mixture and assessed chemoreceptor excitability from the electrical activity in the sinus nerve. Under these conditions they observed transient reduction of chemoreceptor sensitivity to hypoxia. The discrepancy would appear to be explained by the different methods employed.

Despite this slight discrepancy, however, all investigators without exception have found that curare-like substances have considerably less effect on the sensitivity of carotid chemoreceptors to hypoxia than on their sensitivities to acetylcholine and N-cholinomimetic substances.

It should be noted that much larger doses of curare-like substances are required to abolish the sensitivity of N-cholinoreactive systems in the carotid bodies than to block neuromuscular synapses. Consequently, when the animal is completely immobilized by curare-like substances, the carotid chemoreceptors still retain their sensitivity both to hypoxia and to N-cholinomimetic substances.

It is known that much larger doses of curare-like substances are required to block ganglionic N-cholinoreactive systems than to block neuromuscular synapses. It follows, therefore, that the cholinoreactive systems of the carotid bodies are closer in their sensitivity to curare-like substances to the N-cholinoreactive systems in ganglia than to the corresponding systems in striated muscle.

It should be emphasized that diacetylcholines, which do not suppress but rather excite both carotid bodies and ganglia, should be classed as curare-like substances with depolarizing action.

ALKALOIDS OF THE NICOTINE GROUP

Nicotine

The classical investigations of Langley and Dickinson (1889) showed that the most characteristic feature of the action of nicotine is excitation followed by paralysis of sympathetic and parasympathetic ganglia.

In the light of modern concepts, nicotine should be regarded as a cholinomimetic substance, but with an action extending only on some cholinoreactive systems which, because of their selective sensitivity, may be described as nicotine-sensitive or N-cholino-reactive systems. Conversely, nicotine and closely related alkaloids have practically no effect on muscarine-sensitive or M-cholinoreactive systems.

A striking feature in the stage of nicotine absorption is the violent respiratory stimulation. Some of the alkaloids closely related to nicotine, e.g. lobeline, have long been used as respiratory analeptics. The respiratory excitation produced by nicotine was earlier explained by its direct action on the respiratory centre. The decisive part played by reflexes from carotid chemoreceptors in this nicotine effect was first demonstrated by Heymans *et al.* (1931).

An even earlier investigation by father and son (Heymans and Heymans, 1926) had revealed that reflexes from cardio-aortic chemoreceptors play some part in the stimulation of respiration produced by nicotine. Their experiments were carried out on dogs with crossed circulations, the head of the recipient dog being connected with its trunk only through the vagosympathetic nerves. The respiratory movements of the dog with the "isolated" head were intensified by the intravenous injection of relatively large doses of nicotine (2 mg) into its trunk. This effect of nicotine was the result of reflexes from the aortic reflexogenic zone. It was also shown that when nicotine was injected into the blood of the donor dog, even small doses produced violent respiratory movements in the dog with the "isolated" head. The only possible conclusion seemed to be that the effect of nicotine on the respiration was due mainly to its action on the respiratory centre. But later investigations by Heymans *et al.* (1931) indicated that this conclusion was wrong and that the respiratory excitation in the dog with the "isolated head" was the result of reflex effects on the respiratory centre from its carotid sinus reflexogenic zones.

In these experiments the injection of small doses of nicotine (0·002 mg–0·2 mg) into the carotid artery of a dog with a normally innervated sinus led to slow intensification and acceleration of the respiratory movements. Injection of the same doses of nicotine into the carotid artery after denervation of the sinus merely led to slight intensification of respiration after an initial arrest of the respiratory movements.

The importance of reflexes from the carotid sinus zones in the respiratory stimulation produced by nicotine was also demonstrated by Heymans and his co-workers in experiments with the intravenous injection of nicotine. A dose of 2 mg injected into a femoral vein in anaesthetized or unanaesthetized dogs produced powerful respiratory excitation. There was practically no such reaction when the nicotine was injected after denervation of the carotid sinus and cardio-aortic zones.

Finally, the stimulating effect of nicotine on carotid chemoreceptors was demonstrated by the same authors in experiments on dogs in which the isolated carotid sinus was perfused.

Heymans' discovery of the stimulating effect of nicotine on carotid chemoreceptors has been completely confirmed by other investigators. Owen and Gesell (1931) observed respiratory excitation when a nicotine solution was applied to the external surface of the carotid bodies.

Studying the importance of reflex mechanisms in the effect of nicotine on respiration in animals, Anichkov (1934) showed that the respiratory excitation seen when 0·1 mg nicotine was injected intravenously was completely absent or only very slight when the carotid sinuses had been completely removed. Respiratory excitation was only produced in cats with the sinuses removed by a dose five times greater (0·5 mg). It was evident that, with large doses of nicotine, reflexes from other chemoreceptors were involved in the reaction or that nicotine acted directly on the respiratory centre. The direct stimulating effect of nicotine on the respiratory centre has been confirmed by Dubinin (1937).

Heymans et al. (1931) have also shown that nicotine, by its action on the carotid chemoreceptors, produces reflex excitation of the cardiac branches of the vagus nerves and thus slows the heart. The method employed in these experiments was the same as in their investigations on respiratory reflexes. Small doses of nicotine were injected into a carotid artery before and after denervation of the sinus. The substance was injected into a vertebral artery in control experiments. The Belgian authors' experiments proved convincingly that reflex effects on the vagus nerve centres arising from the carotid bodies were concerned in the slowing of the heart produced by nicotine along with the direct excitation of the cardiac ganglia of the vagus nerves. The experiments of Heymans and his co-workers showed that only excessively large doses of nicotine were able directly to excite the cardiac centres of the vagus nerves in the "isolated" head of a dog with the sinuses denervated (see Heymans *et al.*, 1933).

In these same investigations Heymans and his co-workers demonstrated the development of pressor reflexes as a result of the action of nicotine on chemoreceptors. In order to avoid blood pressure changes from other causes, the experiments were carried out on curarized vagotomized dogs on artificial respiration. The carotid sinus was denervated and the external carotid artery was tied on one side, so that all the blood from the common carotid artery on that side went to the brain. On the other side the sinus retained its normal innervation and all the main branches of the common carotid artery were tied so that the substance introduced into it remained as long as possible in the region of the sinus and did not reach the brain. Under these circumstances the injection of even small doses of nicotine into the carotid artery, the sinus of which had a normal nerve supply, produced considerable though transient increase of blood pressure. The injection of similar doses of nicotine into the carotid artery with the sinus denervated or into the vertebral artery produced no change in blood pressure. These experiments demonstrated the extreme sensitivity of the chemoreceptors to the stimulating effect of nicotine, $0 \cdot 1 \, \gamma$ was sufficient to produce reflex hypertension when injected into the common carotid artery with its branches tied. The direct action of nicotine on the vasomotor centre had an incomparably weaker effect and, in the experiments of these same authors, only a dose of 1 mg nicotine directly stimulated effect on the vasomotor centre in the isolated head of the dog, which received its blood supply from the other dog. Other factors such as direct stimulation of the ganglia of sympathetic vasoconstrictor nerves and the direct stimulation of the chromaffin cells in the adrenal medulla are known to be concerned in the pressor effect of nicotine.

The extreme sensitivity of carotid chemoreceptors to nicotine raised the question of the extent to which reflexes from the chemoreceptors were concerned in the pressor effects produced by nicotine. An answer was given by Fedorchuk's experiments (1954) in our laboratory. These experiments were carried out on de- cerebrate cats. Nicotine was injected intravenously before and after removal of the carotid sinuses or before and after blocking of the sinuses, by an injection of a 1% novocaine solution into the surrounding tissue. The minimum effective dose of nicotine (6–8 γ/kg) produced a weak pressor effect before excluding of the sinuses; when the latter had been excluded there was no change in blood pressure. With nicotine in doses of 20–30 γ/kg, the pressor effect with the sinuses intact was three times greater than after their exclusion. There was also a difference in the manner in which the blood pressure rose: the increase induced by nicotine after exclusion of the sinuses developed several seconds later and was more gradual and long-lasting than when the sinuses were normal.

These experiments showed that in the initial stage of the action of nicotine the pressor effect seen with relatively small doses was the result of reflexes from the carotid chemoreceptors, which consequently were more sensitive to nicotine than the adrenals and ganglia. With large doses of nicotine the cholinoreactive systems of these relatively less sensitive tissues were undoubtedly also concerned in the reaction. Fedorchuk also showed that, in decerebrate cats, nicotine in doses which normally produced considerable increase of blood pressure, proved completely in- effective after bilateral adrenalectomy, even though the nerve supplies to the sinuses were intact. It follows, therefore, that the direct reflex from carotid chemoreceptors to the vessels plays a secondary part in the pressor effect that develops when nicotine acts on the carotid bodies; the main cause of the pressor effect is the reflex from the carotid bodies to the suprarenal glands which manifests itself by increase of adrenaline secretion.

The adrenal medulla is probably not the only endocrine gland subject to reflex effects from the carotid chemoreceptors. The water test experiments of Belous (1952, 1953) on dogs showed that the posterior pituitary hypersecretion after cyanide or after small doses of acetylcholine is basically the result of reflexes from the carotid bodies to the posterior lobe of the hypophysis. Belous carried out similar experiments with nicotine. It was injected in

doses of 0·04–0·08 mg/kg intravenously before and after denervation of the carotid sinuses in dogs with the ureters exteriorized. As the same author (Belous, 1948) had shown earlier,
nicotine delayed water diuresis, which was indicative of increased
posterior pituitary secretion. But after denervation of the sinuses,
this response was seen in only four out of eight experimental dogs
and in these it was less. Thus nicotine, unlike cyanide and small
doses of acetylcholine, produces hypersecretion of antidiuretic
hormone (vasopressin) mainly as a result of other factors and not
through a reflex from the carotid bodies. Belous's observations
on dogs with the hypophysis denervated and her experiments in
which the isolated hypophysis was perfused (Belous, 1950) indicate
that the direct action of nicotine on the neurohypophysis is the
factor mainly responsible for this effect.

The different degree to which reflexes from the carotid bodies
contribute to the antidiuretic effects of acetylcholine on the one
hand and of nicotine on the other is probably due to the fact that
nicotine, being the more stable substance, maintains its action for
a longer time, with the result that conditions are more favourable
for a direct action on the hypophysis.

The effects of nicotine on the carotid chemoreceptors described
so far have been concerned only with its stimulating effect and
the reflexes arising therefrom. Yet, the characteristic feature of
nicotine in its selective action on ganglia, on the suprarenal
glands and on myoneural or central synapses is that it has a
diphasic effect. Sudden sharp excitation is followed more or less
rapidly by a block of the cholinoreactive systems, with the result
that the latter become insensitive to the mediator, acetylcholine,
as well as to nicotine itself. Were we able to see a similar second
phase in the action of nicotine on the carotid chemoreceptors?
The best way to decide this was to study the prolonged action
of a given nicotine concentration on the carotid bodies. Suitable
conditions for this can be achieved by perfusion of the isolated
carotid sinuses with nicotine.

Such experiments were carried out on decerebrate cats by our
colleague Asratyan (1938b). Perfusion with nicotine in Ringer–
Locke solution was carried out for short periods in one series of
experiments and for longer periods (4–6 min) in a second series.
Brief perfusion with nicotine solutions in dilutions of from

1:2,000,000 to 1:100,000 produced powerful respiratory excitation. When perfusion with the same nicotine concentrations was continued for longer periods, the initial respiratory stimulation was followed by reduction of both amplitude and rate of the respiratory movements to below the original levels. In this second phase of the action of nicotine on the carotid bodies, there were also changes in the sensitivity to other chemical stimuli: the sensitivity to alkaloids of the nicotine group, anabasine, lobeline, cytisine and others, was particularly reduced. Perfusion with nicotine concentrations of from 1:100,000 to 1:10,000 (1:50,000 was used in most of the experiments) led to the development of a phase of respiratory depression and the carotid bodies ceased entirely to react to nicotine-like alkaloids. Under these conditions respiration was quite unaffected by perfusion of the sinus with solutions of cytisine 1:1,000,000, lobeline 1:500,000, anabasine 1:100,000, coniine 1:12,500 and sparteine 1:10,000—concentrations of the alkaloids which normally produced powerful excitation of the carotid chemoreceptors. Perfusion with nicotine solution 1:50,000 also led to disappearance of the reaction of the carotid chemoreceptors to tetramethylammonium iodide 1:10,000. Prolonged flushing of the sinuses with pure Ringer–Locke fluid restored the sensitivity to these poisons in most experiments.

Parallel experiments were carried out to investigate the effect of nicotine on the sensitivity of the carotid bodies to acetylcholine, carbon dioxide and potassium cyanide. The experimental procedure was exactly the same. Acetylcholine was used in dilutions of 1:1,000,000–1:100,000; perfusion of the isolated sinus with these produced vigorous respiratory stimulation. When, in the course of a perfusion of the sinus with nicotine 1:50,000, the second phase in the action of nicotine developed, the same solutions of acetylcholine produced much less pronounced effects. Fair responses to acetylcholine developed in only three of the twelve experiments, and even then this was very much attenuated; the stimulating effect of acetylcholine was barely appreciable in five experiments and entirely absent in four.

Different results were obtained when carbon dioxide and cyanide were tested after exposure of the sinus to nicotine. Ringer–Locke solution saturated with carbon dioxide was prepared by passing carbon dioxide for 1–2 min through the solution before the experiment. Solution sufficient for the whole experiment was prepared at a time but the pH was tested before each perfusion; for this a sample was taken just before it entered the sinus. The normal pH of the Ringer–Locke solution in these experiments was 7·2–7·3, when saturated with carbon dioxide it was between 5·6 and 6·7. The pH remained constant throughout each experiment. The perfusion of carbon dioxide-saturated Ringer–Locke solution through the isolated sinus normally produced reflex respiratory excitation. The effects of this saturation were tested before and after exposure of the sinus to nicotine (1:10,000–1:50,000) in ten experiments. The nicotine perfusion was continued until the second depressive phase of its action was attained (3–9 min). Under these conditions the sensitivity of the carotid bodies to carbon dioxide was then reduced, but not to the same extent as that for alkaloids of the nicotine group or for acetylcholine. The acidified fluid produced no effect after perfusion with nicotine 1:50,000 in only one out of ten experiments. In the remaining nine the reaction was either only slightly weakened or the same as before exposure to nicotine.

Similar results were obtained by Asratyan in experiments on the effect of nicotine on the sensitivity of the carotid chemoreceptors to cyanide. Perfusion of the isolated sinus in decerebrate cats with potassium cyanide solutions 1:100,000–1:5000 for 20–40 sec produced powerful respiratory excitation. To exclude any possibility that the potassium ions affected the chemoreceptors, the potassium chloride content of the Ringer–Locke solution in which the potassium cyanide was dissolved was correspondingly reduced. After a preliminary test of the sensitivity of the carotid chemoreceptors to cyanide, nicotine (1:75,000–1:20,000) was perfused through the isolated sinus. The perfusion was continued until there was a distinct development of the phase of depression (3–6 min), after which the sinus was again perfused with the same cyanide solution. In all four such experiments potassium cyanide produced somewhat feebler effects after nicotine perfusion, but complete disappearance of sensitivity to cyanide was not observed.

Asratyan's experiments thus indicate that, with the advent of the second phase in the action of nicotine on the carotid chemoreceptors, the latter lost their sensitivity for alkaloids of the

H

nicotine group (anabasine, lobeline, cytisine and sparteine) and there was a reduction of the sensitivity to carbon dioxide, cyanide and more particularly to acetylcholine.

Asratyan examined the effect of nicotine on the carotid baroreceptors in the same investigation. Nicotine was found to have no effect on the reactivity of the baroreceptors and their reaction to reduced blood pressure was just as before.

Despite the carefulness and completeness of Asratyan's analysis of the effect of nicotine on the carotid receptors, no definite conclusions can be drawn from his work. The transition from the initial excitation to the phase of depression observed by him in the action of nicotine might have been due to a lowered excitability of the respiratory centre and not on changes in the reactivity of the chemoreceptors themselves. The reduced response to other poisons could be explained in the same way. Again, the occurrence of slight respiratory excitation when a poison was perfused through the isolated carotid sinus cannot be ascribed with certainty to the effect of the poison on the carotid bodies, as there may have been slight escape of the perfusion fluid into the general circulation, a possibility which it is extremely difficult to avoid altogether even when the sinus is prepared with the greatest of care.

Much more accurate results can be obtained when the excitability of the carotid receptors is assessed from the electrical activity in the sinus nerve, particularly when the method developed by Krylov is used. On the completely isolated sinus, Krylov analysed the effect of nicotine on the carotid chemoreceptors and showed that when the completely isolated sinus was perfused outside the body with nicotine, 200 γ being injected into the perfusion fluid, there was a burst of impulses in the sinus nerve. The electrical activity in the nerve is of the same character as when the carotid chemoreceptors are excited by other chemical stimuli. When the isolated sinus was perfused with comparatively strong nicotine solutions (a 1:25,000 solution of nicotine base), there was an increase in the amplitude of the potentials in the sinus nerve only during the initial period of perfusion; electrical activity declined after 3–5 min and the nicotine-induced discharges ceased.

The sensitivity of the carotid bodies to acetylcholine was

tested by injecting 20 γ into the perfusion fluid. This dose, injected when the sinus was being perfused with pure Ringer–Locke solution, produced sharp excitation of the chemoreceptors and a corresponding increase of electrical activity in the sinus nerve. Injection of the same dose of acetylcholine during the stage of depression produced by nicotine had no stimulating effect on the chemoreceptors.

Krylov carried out similar experiments to test the sensitivity of the carotid chemoreceptors to potassium cyanide. Cyanide, 200 γ injected into the fluid perfusing the carotid sinus, produced considerable acceleration and increase in amplitude of the potentials in the sinus nerve before exposure to nicotine. The same cyanide effect was observed after the chemoreceptors had been depressed by exposure to nicotine (1:25,000).

When depressed by nicotine, the chemoreceptors lose their sensitivity to acetylcholine but retain sensitivity to the hypoxic poison cyanide and also to potassium ions (Fig. 11).

Synthetic Isomers and Derivatives of Nicotine

Heymans and Booker (1941) investigated α-nicotine (2-pyridyl-α-methylpyrrolidine), a synthetic isomer of nicotine. Like natural nicotine, this compound excites the carotid chemoreceptors but its action is much weaker than that of nicotine and doses several times larger (1·3 mg/kg α-nicotine as compared with 0·07–0·3 mg/kg natural β-nicotine) are required to produce respiratory stimulation in dogs. When the methylpyrrolidine group was shifted from the β to the α position, both the stimulating effect on N-cholinoreactive receptors and toxicity were reduced. The synthetic α-nicotine was found to be five to six times less toxic than the natural alkaloid in experiments on various animals.

Aminonicotines and their acetyl derivatives have been studied in detail (Mednikyan, 1936).

These compounds were found to have nicotine-like properties in greater or lesser degree and stimulated respiration in the stage of their absorption but were much inferior to the original alkaloid in this respect. At the same time all these compounds are less toxic than nicotine. Mednikyan (1936) found that the stimulating effect of α-acetylaminonicotine on respiration was almost 300 times less than that of nicotine but that it was less toxic than nicotine to almost the same extent. It follows, therefore, that the therapeutic range of α-acetylaminonicotine as a respiratory analeptic is not greater than that of nicotine. Mednikyan's experiments would, however, indicate that this nicotine derivative has a certain advantage over nicotine and lobeline as respiratory stimulants. Its intravenous injection is not generally followed by

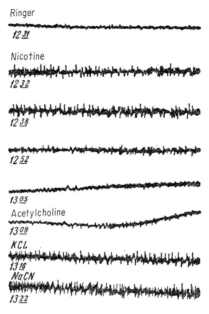

FIG. 11. Isolated carotid sinus of the cat outside the body. Recording of electrical activity in the sinus nerve. Injection into the perfusing fluid of 0·4 ml of each of the following solutions: acetylcholine (1/10,000), potassium chloride (1/100) and sodium cyanide (1/10,000) during perfusion of the sinus with nicotine 1/500,000 solution.

initial arrest of respiration and the respiratory stimulation is not accompanied by any serious increase of blood pressure and lasts longer than the stimulation produced by the injection of lobeline. Mednikyan demonstrated the reasons for this in special experiments: the inactivation of effective doses of α-acetylaminonicotine was ten times slower than the inactivation of nicotine, lobeline or anabasine.

Mednikyan recommended α'-acetylaminonicotine for clinical use as a respiratory analeptic to replace lobeline.

Under the name peracetin, the preparation has been used by a number of clinicians as a respiratory stimulant and has been reported on favourably.

The intravenous injection of peracetin together with lobeline has been suggested for estimation of the rate of blood flow. Experiments on the dog would indicate that peracetin has the advantage that, in small doses, it does not produce any increase of blood pressure (Gordienko and Nazarova, 1944).

The pharmacology of α'-aminonicotine and its acetyl derivatives has also been investigated by Arbuzov (1945), who compared the activities of laevorotatory and dextrorotatory isomers of these compounds. He examined L-α'-aminonicotine, D-α'-amino-nicotine, L-acetyl-α'-aminonicotine and D-acetyl-α'-aminonicotine. Among other pharmacological properties, the action of these substances on the carotid bodies was investigated by injection of solutions into the fluid perfusing the isolated sinus in the cat.

All preparations produced reflex excitation of respiration, the aminonicotines being more active than their acetyl derivatives and the laevorotatory isomer in each pair being more active than the dextrorotatory. This was also true of the toxicity of these compounds. The relationship between intensity of action on the carotid bodies and toxicity varied, however, with different substances.

Dextrorotatory α'-aminonicotine was found to be only slightly toxic and yet have quite a powerful effect on the carotid bodies. Arbuzov draws attention to the possible use of this substance as a respiratory analeptic.

Anabasine and its Derivatives

The alkaloid anabasine (synonyms: nicotimine, neonicotine) was isolated by Orekhov (1921) from a Central Asian plant, *Anabasis aphylla* L. Chemically, it is α-piperidyl-β-pyridine. Pure anabasine is a colourless oily liquid, soluble in water. Sargin (1934) and Haag (1933) have described it as having pharmacological properties similar to those of nicotine. The selective action of anabasine on carotid chemoreceptors was first demonstrated by Anichkov (Anichkov, 1934, 1935, 1937; Anichkov and Pleshchitser, 1935; Anichkov *et al.*, 1936).

In experiments on dogs under morphine and on decerebrate cats the intravenous injection of anabasine, 0·04–0·15 mg/kg produced powerful respiratory stimulation after the usual transient arrest of respiration typical of nicotine-like substances. The respiratory arrest is due to a reflex from the sensory endings of the pulmonary branches of the vagus nerves, and is absent in vagotomized animals. Respiratory excitation did not develop when the same doses of anabasine were injected into animals from which the carotid sinuses had been removed (Fig. 12).

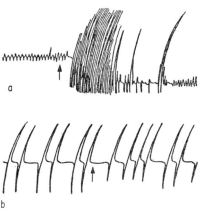

FIG. 12. Dog (5·2 kg) under morphine (0·04 g subcutaneously). a—intravenous injection of anabasine (0·2 mg/kg). b—the same after extirpation of the carotid sinuses and bilateral vagotomy. The arrows indicate the injection of anabasine.

The injection of very small doses of anabasine (5 γ) directly into the common carotid artery, the nerve supply of which was intact, led to slow development of powerful respiratory excitation in decerebrate cats. Injection of the same dose into the denervated carotid artery or into the vertebral artery was without effect.

These experiments indicate that the respiratory excitation induced by anabasine is mainly due to reflexes from the carotid chemoreceptors. Doses of anabasine ten times greater were required to produce respiratory excitation when injected into the vertebral artery, the effect in this case was obviously due to direct action on the respiratory centre. The direct excitatory effect of anabasine on the respiratory centre can also be observed when very large doses are injected intravenously into vagotomized animals with the carotid sinuses removed.

Reflex respiratory excitation can be produced by the action of anabasine on the isolated carotid sinus. Asratyan's (1938b) experiments were carried out on the carotid sinus of decerebrate cats by the perfusion method usually adopted in our laboratory. In these experiments anabasine produced excitation of the carotid chemoreceptors when the isolated sinus was perfused with dilutions of 1:1,000,000 or less. With strong anabasine solutions (1:50,000) the very pronounced initial excitation was followed after a few minutes by reduction in the amplitude and rate of respiration, with ultimate return to the normal initial level. In other words, prolonged perfusion of the carotid sinus with strong anabasine solutions led to loss of the stimulating effect on the chemoreceptors. Anichkov found in his experiments (1935) that the excitatory effect of anabasine on respiration was one-fourth of that of nicotine.

Discovery of the stimulating effect of anabasine on the carotid chemoreceptors led to an examination of a number of its derivatives to determine their usefulness as respiratory analeptics.

A number of Soviet scientists have investigated the pharmacology of N-methylanabasine, which differs in structure from anabasine in the same way as nicotine from nornicotine. When a methyl group is attached to nornicotine (change over from nornicotine to nicotine) the toxicity diminishes but the excitatory effect on cholinoreactive systems is increased (Bovet and Bovet-Nitti, 1948). It might be expected that the same pattern would be repeated in the change from anabasine to N-methylanabasine and that the introduction of a methyl group on the nitrogen would render the effect of the substance less toxic and at the same time more powerfully stimulating to respiration. This was not, however, found to be so. All authors who have examined the pharmacology of N-methylanabasine are agreed that it is less toxic and a weaker respiratory stimulant than anabasine (Syrneva, 1938; Poluektov, 1946; Saksonov, 1946; Mashkovskii, 1943).

Comparing the toxicity and pharmocological properties of anabasine with those of methylanabasine, Poluektov found that the latter was four times less toxic than anabasine (subcutaneous injection in mouse experiments) and that the stimulating effect on respiration of methylanabasine was but one twenty-fifth of that of anabasine (intravenous injection in experiments on decerebrate cats). If these findings are correct, methylanabasine has no advantage over anabasine and cannot be recommended as a respiratory analeptic.

Mashkovskii came to the same conclusion. Saksonov formed a different opinion from his experiments. He found that there was a very wide interval between the minimum doses of methylanabasine producing respiratory stimulation when injected intravenously and the doses producing toxic effects when injected into the same animals by the same route. According to his experiments, a dose of 0·15 mg/kg produced appreciable increase in the volume of respiration and toxic phenomena (muscular twitching, vomiting, intermittent respiration and convulsions) developed when a dose of 4 mg/kg was administered by the same route. Saksonov compared his findings with published accounts of the analeptic effect of lobeline and Peracetin; he found that methylanabasine was superior to these substances and, therefore, recommended it as a respiratory analeptic.

Other anabasine derivatives which have been submitted to detailed pharmacological examination are α-aminoanabasine and its acetyl derivative (Poluektov, 1935; Raspopova, 1955).

Poluektov found that the introduction of an amino group in the α-position in the pyridine ring of the anabasine molecule reduced the toxicity of the latter by half (subcutaneous injection in experiments on mice) and its stimulating effect on respiration (intravenous injection in experiments on decerebrate cats) by three-fourths. Poluektov noted that the initial respiratory arrest associated with intravenous injection was less pronounced with the amino derivative than with anabasine itself.

Otherwise, according to Poluektov, there were no qualitative pharmacological differences between anabasine and α-amino-anabasine. When α-aminoanabasine was acetylated, its toxicity became even less but there was still greater reduction in its stimulating effect on respiration. Raspopova's experiments indicated that the toxicity of acetyl-α-aminoanabasine for mice when injected subcutaneously was two to three times less than the toxicity of α-aminoanabasine and five to six times less than that of anabasine itself. In order to produce definite respiratory excitation in anaesthetized cats and rabbits, 20 mg/kg acetyl-α-aminoanabasine had to be injected intravenously, a dose about thirty times greater than the corresponding does of α-aminoanabasine and 100 times or more greater than the dose of anabasine producing the same effect.

Consideration of all the existing evidence on these derivatives of anabasine leads to the conclusion that the introduction of methyl groups on the nitrogen or of amino groups in the α-position in the pyridine ring or, again, the acetylation of the latter reduces the stimulating effect of anabasine on respiration considerably or, in other words, weakens its effect on the carotid chemoreceptors.

Coniine

Coniine, the alkaloid of hemlock (*Conium maculatum* L.) is a piperidine derivative, like anabasine and lobeline; it is α-propyl-piperidine.

Coniine is classified as a typical nicotine-like poison, acting on all N-cholinoreactive systems. It could therefore be expected that its selective action would also involve the carotid chemo-receptors. This action was proved by Anichkov and his co-workers in 1935 in experiments on decerebrate cats (see Anichkov, 1937; Anichkov *et al.*, 1936) and also by Dautrebande and Philli-pot, 1935) on dogs.

Coniine 0·2 mg/kg injected intravenously into a decerebrate cat with the nerve-supply to the carotid sinus intact produced powerful dyspnoea but the same dose injected into an animal in which the sinuses had been removed had no effect on respiration.

The stimulating effect of coniine on the carotid chemoreceptors was demonstrated by Anichkov in experiments on decerebrate cats in which the isolated sinus was perfused. Intensification of respiration was observed in some experiments when the isolated sinus was perfused with 1:1,000,000 coniine solution, and in a dilution of 1:100,000 coniine produced powerful reflex respiratory excitation in all experiments without exception. This effect was not observed when the coniine solution was perfused through the isolated sinus after the latter had been treated with procaine.

Asratyan (1938b) carried out experiments in which the isolated sinus of the decerebrate cat was perfused with coniine solutions for longer periods. After coniine had been acting for several minutes the carotid chemoreceptors became temporarily insensitive to subsequent action of the same poison. The coniine effect on the carotid chemoreceptors was thus diphasic, the stage of chemoreceptor excitation being followed by a stage of reduced sensitivity.

Lobeline

Lobeline, the main alkaloid of *Lobelia inflata*, is a derivative of N-methylpiperidine.

Heymans *et al.* (1931) tested lobeline when they were investigating the mode of action of nicotine. They proved that lobeline, like nicotine, has a stimulating effect on respiration, mainly through its action on the carotid chemoreceptors. The method employed to demonstrate the stimulating effect of lobeline on the carotid chemoreceptors was the same as in these authors' experiments with nicotine and cyanides. Small doses of lobeline (0·1 mg), injected into the common carotid artery of the dog, produced powerful respiratory stimulation. Injection of the same or even of a larger dose into a carotid artery in which the sinus had been denervated or into a vertebral artery produced no stimulation and might even depress respiration. Respiratory stimulation was not observed or was very slight and delayed when lobeline was injected intravenously into dogs in which the carotid and aortic reflexogenic zones had been denervated. Heymans obtained these results in experiments on both anaesthetized and unanaesthetized animals.

Heymans concluded that the earlier concepts of a direct stimulating effect of lobeline on the respiratory centre were untenable and that lobeline stimulated respiration reflexly by its action on the carotid chemoreceptors.

Heymans *et al.* also showed that the action of lobeline on the carotid chemoreceptors led to a reflex increase of blood pressure and reflex bradycardia (Heymans *et al.*, 1931c).

These vascular and cardiac reflexes were observed when small doses of lobeline (0·01 mg) were injected into a common carotid artery with its nerve supply intact; they were not seen when the sinus had been denervated. It was found that the cardiac and vascular reflexes produced by lobeline from the carotid chemoreceptors were not connected with the respiratory changes, as the former could be observed in dogs with the spinal cord transsected in the cervical region and the latter in curarized animals.

In Heymans' experiments only very large doses of lobeline had a direct stimulating effect on the centres for the cardiac branches of the vagus nerves and on the vasomotor centre.

Asratyan (1938b) studied the action of lobeline hydrochloride on the isolated carotid sinus during perfusion with Ringer–Locke solution. The weakest solution of lobeline hydrochloride causing respiratory excitation when perfused through the isolated sinus in the decerebrate cat was a dilution of 1:5,000,000. In this strength lobeline produced reflex increase of the depth of respiration; stronger solutions (1:2,000,000–1:100,000,000) also increased the rate of respiration. The respiratory stimulation continued for the entire period of lobeline perfusion (5–7 min), and there was no subsequent depression.

The stimulating effect of lobeline on the carotid chemoreceptors has also been demonstrated by Swedish authors (Euler et al., 1939, 1941a) by oscillographic recording from the sinus nerve. They injected small doses of lobeline into a carotid artery of the cat and observed increase of electrical activity in the sinus nerve. Other authors (Gayet and Quivy, 1934; Velasquez, 1941) have confirmed this and there is now no doubt that a reflex mechanism is responsible for the stimulating effect of lobeline on respiration.

Lobelia contains, in addition to lobeline, a number of alkaloids chemically related to lobeline, including lobelanine and lobelanidine. The former has a keto group and the latter a hydroxyl group in each of the side chains, whereas lobeline has a keto group in one of its side chains and a hydroxyl group in another. Both these alkaloids thus differ from lobeline in the symmetry of their molecules. Lobelane, which differs from lobeline in the absence of both keto and hydroxyl groups, has been obtained synthetically. Zakusov (1934, 1935) has examined the effects of all these three symmetrical alkaloids of the lobeline series on respiration.

Lobelane, lobelanine and lobelanidine were found to have effects which were only one-tenth or one-twelfth that of lobeline and, when injected intravenously, only produced respiratory excitation in doses which were toxic. It can, therefore, be concluded that substances similar in structure to lobeline but differing in having symmetrical molecules have much weaker stimulating effects on the carotid chemoreceptors. It may be noted that these three alkaloids, lobelane, lobelanine and lobelanidine, reduce blood pressure instead of giving the characteristic pressor lobeline effect. These substances are also, apparently, much inferior to lobeline in their stimulating effects on other N-cholinoreactive systems.

It is of some interest to compare the pharmacological activity of lobelane, lobelanine and lobelanidine with that of two other alkaloids of the same lobeline series, lobinine and isolobeline.

The side chains of these two alkaloids, like those of lobeline, differ from one another. Both these alkaloids with asymmetrical molecules have powerful stimulating effects on respiration (see Bovet and Bovet-Nitti, 1948). The powerful excitatory effect of isolobeline on the carotid chemoreceptors has been demonstrated by Pannier and Backer (1945).

Zakusov has likewise tested the effect on respiration of norlobeline, which differs from lobeline in the absence of a methyl group attached to the nitrogen.

Norlobeline was found to be much inferior to lobeline in its effect on respiration. The addition of a methyl group to the nitrogen has thus a completely different effect on the carotid chemoreceptors in the two piperidine derivatives, anabasine and norlobeline. In the former the introduction of a methyl group on the nitrogen of the piperidine ring reduced activity to a small fraction of its former value whereas the presence of a methyl group in the same position in lobeline increased its action on the carotid chemoreceptors considerably.

Cytisine and Methylcytisine

Cytisine is a vegetable alkaloid, found particularly in *Cytisus laburnum* L., from which its name is derived.

Basically, the cytisine molecule consists of two condensed piperidine rings. Cytisine can, however, be regarded as a lupinane derivative.

The pharmacological properties of cytisine were first described in detail by Dale and Laidlaw (1910). Like other substances with nicotine-like properties, cytisine has a selective action on the carotid chemoreceptors, an effect first demonstrated by Anichkov (1937).

Cytisine 0·8 γ/kg injected into a femoral vein in a decerebrate cat with intact carotid sinuses produced powerful respiratory excitation, an effect completely absent when the carotid sinuses had been removed. The excitatory effect of cytisine on the carotid chemoreceptors was demonstrated by experiments in which the isolated carotid sinus was perfused in decerebrate cats. In Anichkov's experiments reflex respiratory excitation was seen when the isolated sinus was perfused with cytisine 1:1,000,000. Asratyan's experiments (1938) showed that this was not the minimum effective concentration; respiratory excitation could be observed in decerebrate cats when the isolated sinus was perfused with cytisine 1:2,000,000.

Cytisine is thus one of the most powerful carotid chemoreceptor stimulators.

In the action of cytisine on the carotid chemoreceptors, as in that of other nicotine-like substances, the phase of excitation is followed by a phase of reduced receptor excitability. In Asratyan's experiments excitation during cytisine perfusion declined and the chemoreceptors ceased to react even to stronger cytisine solutions.

The selective action of cytisine on the carotid chemoreceptors and the resulting reflex excitation of respiration led Mashkovskii (1941) to suggest its use in conjunction with lobeline as a respiratory analeptic. In cats the stimulating effect on respiration produced by intravenous injection was twenty times greater with cytisine than with lobeline whereas the toxicity of the former was only eight to ten times greater than that of lobeline when injected subcutaneously into mice, rats and rabbits.

The therapeutic range of cytisine as a respiratory analeptic is thus, according to Mashkovskii's results, approximately twice that of lobeline.

As suggested by Mashkovskii, a 0·15% solution of cytisine is used under the name of Cytiton as a respiratory analeptic. It is recommended that Cytiton should be injected in doses of 0·5–1·0 ml intravenously or 1 ml intramuscularly.

The intramuscular injection of therapeutic doses of either

Cytiton or lobeline was found in investigations carried out in Prof. Mikhel'son's laboratory on volunteers (see Mikhel'son *et al.*, 1957) to have no effect on respiration; the only effective method was intravenous injection. An undoubted advantage of Cytiton over lobeline for Soviet medicine is the availability and cheapness of plant material such as *Thermopsis lanceolata*, the seeds of which contain cytisine and which grows wild over large areas of Siberia. *Thermopsis lanceolata* also contains the alkaloid N-methylcytisine, which is similar to cytisine in pharmacological properties but much less powerful (Yuzbashinskaya, 1938). The action of methylcytisine on respiration, that is on the carotid chemoreceptors, is approximately twenty times weaker than that of cytisine.

The attachment of a methyl group to the nitrogen thus has the same reducing effect on the activity of cytisine as on that of anabasine, whereas the presence of this group in the structures of nicotine and lobeline has the opposite effect, an intensifying effect on the carotid bodies.

Sparteine, Pachycarpine, Piperidine and Trimethylamine

Sparteine is the alkaloid of the plants *Sarothamnus scoparius* and *Lupinus luteus* and it is also present in some other leguminous plants. Chemically sparteine, like cytisine, is regarded as a lupinane derivative, having two condensed piperidine rings in its molecule. Sparteine differs from cytisine in that it is a completely saturated oxygen-free compound and consists of four, and not three, rings.

In its pharmacological properties sparteine has long been regarded as a nicotine-like "ganglionic" poison (Dixon, 1924), but it has a very much less powerful effect on ganglia than nicotine or cytisine, to which it is particularly close in structure.

Sparteine also has a nicotine-like effect on the carotid chemoreceptors, although this is relatively weak. Intravenous injection into experimental animals was followed by transient respiratory excitation. Zunz and Tremonti (1931) were the first to show that this effect was a reflex from the carotid sinuses: sparteine elicited no respiratory excitation after denervation of the sinuses in dogs anaesthetized with chloralose and in rabbits under morphine.

The direct stimulating effect of sparteine on the carotid chemoreceptors was demonstrated by Asratyan (1938b) in experiments on decerebrate cats. He showed that perfusion of the isolated carotid sinus caused reflex respiratory excitation. The lowest effective concentration of sparteine sulphate was found to be 1:100,000, or 200 times stronger than that of cytisine. Asratyan found that when the isolated sinus had been perfused with this solution for 90 sec, the sensitivity of the carotid chemoreceptors began to decline.

Sparteine is, therefore, much inferior to the other alkaloids of the nicotine group in its stimulating effect on both the carotid chemoreceptors and other cholinoreactive systems. The second, depressive, phase in its action is pronounced.

Pachycarpine is an alkaloid isolated by Academician A. P. Orekhov and his co-workers from the leaves and stalks of the plant *Sophora pachycarpa* and also from the leaves of *Thermopsis lanceolata* and is the stereoisomer of sparteine. Sparteine is laevo-rotatory and pachycarpine dextrorotatory.

Mashkovskii and Rabkina (1952) made a pharmacological study of pachycarpine iodate. They found that the intravenous injection of pachycarpin in doses of not less than 0·5 mg/kg in curarized cats led to considerable reduction of the reaction to the subsequent intravenous injection of cytisine (0·03–0·04 mg/kg) and, after the injection of 5 mg/kg pachycarpine, cytisine had practically no effect on the nictitating membrane, blood pressure or respiration.

These experiments indicate that pachycarpine is very similar to its stereoisomer, sparteine, in its ability to block N-cholino-reactive systems, including those of the carotid bodies.

The results obtained by Mashkovskii and Rabkina (1952) suggest that the initial stage of excitation of the N-cholinoreactive systems in ganglia, in the suprarenal glands and in the carotid bodies is more pronounced with pachycarpine than with sparteine.

Coniine and lobeline are piperidine derivatives. The molecules of cytisine and sparteine contain two condensed piperidine rings. The nicotine molecule contains a five-membered homologue of piperidine, pyrrolidine.

Piperidine itself is known to possess some, though very slight, nicotine-like action.

Piperidine also has a stimulating effect on the N-cholino-reactive systems in the carotid bodies. Dautrebande and Phillipot

(1935) and Gernandt (1946) have shown that the weak stimulating effect of piperidine on respiration is due to reflexes from the carotid sinuses.

The alkaloids of the nicotine group have tertiary amino groups in their molecule. Piperidine itself is a tertiary amine. One of the simplest tertiary amines, trimethylamine, also has some nicotine-like pharmacological properties. Mercier *et al.* (1934) have shown that trimethylamine does not produce respiratory excitation if the carotid sinuses of the experimental animals have previously been denervated. Even this tertiary amine of simple structure apparently has a stimulating effect on the carotid bodies.

Comparative Intensities of the Effects
of Various N-Cholinomimetic Substances on the Carotid Bodies

All these findings on the effects on the carotid chemoreceptors of a large number of plant alkaloids and synthetic amines with nicotine-like properties, that is selective stimulation on N-cholinoreactive systems, indicate that stimulation of the carotid bodies is an invariable feature of substances of this type. It is of interest to compare the stimulating effect of substances of this group on the carotid chemoreceptors with their effects on synaptic N-cholinergic systems.

Such a comparison was made by Asratyan (1938b), when he compared the effects of certain alkaloids of the nicotine group on the carotid chemoreceptors with those on the suprarenals and autonomic ganglia. For the comparison he used the results of his own experiments on the perfused isolated sinuses of the cat, the results obtained in our laboratory by Kuznetsov (1928) on the latter perfused isolated suprarenals in cattle and Dixon's findings (1924) for the action of same alkaloids on ganglia, as given in Heffter's handbook.

We give below figures from Asratyan's paper for the minimum effective concentrations of alkaloids of the nicotine group acting on the carotid chemoreceptors.

These alkaloids are arranged in order of the intensity of their action on the suprarenals as found in Kuznetsov's experiments. Cytisine, nicotine and lobeline are powerful stimulants, coniine and sparteine are weaker, and gelsemine is much weaker. Finally, the intensities of the effects of these same substances on ganglia

Alkaloid	Minimum effective concentration
Cytisine nitrate	1 : 20,000,000
Tetramethylammonium iodide	1 : 10,000,000
Lobeline hydrochloride	1 : 5,000,000
Nicotine—base	1 : 20,000,000
Anabasine—base	1 : 1,000,000
Coniine—base	1 : 500,000
Sparteine sulphate	1 : 100,000

Substance	Paralysing effect on CNS	Action on sympathetic ganglia
Cytisine ⎫ Nicotine ⎬	Very positive	Very definite
Lobeline		All stimulate and then paralyse, in the same order of potency as for the CNS
Coniine	Weak	
Piperidine	Very weak	
Sparteine	Weak	Weak
Gelsemine	Distinct	Distinct

and the central nervous system as found by Dixon are compared.

These comparisons indicate that the effects of alkaloids of the nicotine group on the carotid chemoreceptors, autonomic ganglia and the suprarenal glands are similar in both character and relative intensity. This is a further proof of the presence in the carotid bodies of N-cholinoreactive systems similar to those found in ganglia.

SYNTHETIC CHOLINOLYTICS WITH M- AND N-CHOLINOLYTIC PROPERTIES

Numerous preparations with cholinolytic properties have been synthesized in the last 20 years and introduced into therapeutic practice as substitutes for atropine. Unlike atropine, most of them have in addition to their action on M-cholinoreactive systems, a pronounced blocking effect on N-cholinoreactive systems. Some of the synthetic cholinolytics with a tertiary nitrogen in their

I

structure, e.g. Trasentin, Diphacil (Spasmolytin) or Pentaphen (Parpanit) act mainly on central interneuron cholinergic synapses (see Anichkov, 1959, 1960). Their quaternary derivatives, on the other hand, have more powerful actions on peripheral M- and N-cholinoreactive systems and weaker central effects (Mikhel'son et al., 1957).

A number of synthetic cholinolytics which act on both M- and N-cholinoreactive systems have been tested for their effects on the carotid chemoreceptors.

The action of the hydrochloride of the diphenyl acetic ester of diethylaminoethanol (Diphacil) has been studied in our laboratory by Tomilina (1951, 1952).

By perfusing the isolated sinus in decerebrate cats she established that the passage of Diphacil solutions of 1:500,000 or less rendered the chemoreceptors insensitive to both acetylcholine and nicotine. Comparison of these findings with those obtained by the same method by Polyakov-Stanevich (1938a) indicates that Diphacil has a much more powerful blocking effect on N-cholinoreactive systems in the carotid bodies than atropine, which reduces carotid body sensitivity to acetylcholine only in dilutions of 1:100,000. At the same time the experiments of Tomilina (1952) indicate that Diphacil is approximately fifty times weaker than atropine in its effect on M-cholinoreactive systems and that it differs from atropine in having a considerable blocking effect on N-cholinoreactive systems. The blocking effect of Diphacil on the carotid chemoreceptors can thus be linked with action on N- and not on M-cholinoreactive systems.

The effects of some of the newer synthetic cholinolytics have been studied in Mikhel'son's laboratory (Tsirk, 1957). Tsirk used as the index of a block of the N-cholinoreactive systems in the carotid chemoreceptors the absence of a respiratory reaction to the intravenous injection of Corconium (diiodide of dicholine ester of suberic acid). Corconium has a powerful N-cholinomimetic action and it produces respiratory excitation by a reflex from the carotid bodies. Corconium has the advantage over nicotine that, because of its rapid destruction by cholinesterase, it can be injected repeatedly and will invariably produce the same effect.

The following synthetic cholinolytic preparations have been tested: Pentaphen (hydrochloride of the diethylaminoethyl ester of phenylcyclopentane carboxylic acid), Diphasin (hydrochloride of diethylaminoacetyl-N-phenothiazine), α-methyl-Diphasin (hydrochloride of a Diphasin derivative with a methyl group in the α-position in relation to the nitrogen in the aminoacetyl part of the molecule) and Arpenal (hydrochloride of diethylaminopropylamide of diphenylacetic acid). In addition to these tertiary amines their quaternary analogues were also studied (iodomethylate and iodoethylate of each of the esters and the methylsulphomethylates of Pentaphen and Diphasin).

The experiments were carried out on cats under hexabarbitol (150 mg/kg) intravenously or anaesthetized with urethane (1 g per animal intraperitoneally). Corconium (0·01 mg/kg in 1:10,000 solution) was injected intravenously.

All these compounds were found to block N-cholinoreactive systems in the carotid bodies and, when injected intravenously, they prevented the development of a respiratory reaction to the injection of Corconium.

We gave the minimum doses of the preparations (mg/kg) that prevented the respiratory effect of Corconium.

Pentaphen	5·0 mg/kg
its iodomethylate	3·0 mg/kg
its iodoethylate	3·0 mg/kg
Diphasin	10·0 mg/kg
its iodomethylate	5·0 mg/kg
its iodoethylate	3·0 mg/kg
α-methyl-Diphasin	7·0–8·0 mg/kg
its iodomethylate	2·0 mg/kg
its iodoethylate	3·0–4·0 mg/kg
Arpenal	5·0 mg/kg
its iodomethylate	2·0 mg/kg
its iodoethylate	2·0 mg/kg

While investigating the effects of these cholinolytics on the respiratory excitation produced by corconium, the author also examined their actions on the pressor effect and the contraction of the nictitating membrane produced by Corconium. According to findings obtained in Mikhel'son's laboratory, these effects of Corconium depend on its action on N-cholinoreactive systems in the sympathetic ganglia and adrenal glands. It was found that the doses of the cholinolytics which blocked N-cholinoreactive systems in the carotid bodies also prevented these Corconium effects. As with other cholinomimetic and cholinolytic substances, the effects of these cholinolytics on the cholinoreactive systems in the carotid bodies ran parallel with their effects on the cholinoreactive systems in the ganglia and suprarenal glands.

ANTICHOLINESTERASES

The effect of the cholinesterase inhibitor, physostigmine, on the carotid bodies was first studied by Polyakov (1938a). He found that perfusion of the isolated sinus of the decerebrate cat with a solution of 1:100,000 of physostigmine salicylate considerably increased the sensitivity of chemoreceptors to acetylcholine. The chemoreceptors reacted to acetylcholine solution in dilution not greater than 1:100,000 when the sinus was perfused with pure Ringer–Locke solution but in the presence of physostigmine 1:100,000,000 acetylcholine had an appreciable stimulating effect on the sinus chemoreceptors and led to reflex respiratory excitation.

The results obtained by Polyakov with physostigmine have since been confirmed by many authors with other anticholinesterases.

Sensitization of the carotid bodies to acetylcholine on exposure to physostigmine or Proserine has been demonstrated by Kaindl and Werner (1936), Schweitzer and Wright (1938) and Heymans et al. (1953). Verbeke (1949a, 1949b) and Douglas (1952a) found that di-isopropylfluorophosphate (DFP) and tetraethylpyrophosphate (TEPP) increased the acetylcholine sensitivity of the carotid bodies sharply. Hexaethyltetraphosphate (HETP) and No. 683 have been found to have similar effects (Verbeke and Votava, 1949; Caldeyro and Garcia Austt, 1949; Mazella and Migliaro, 1949; Fernandez, 1949). Increase of the carotid body sensitivity to acetylcholine as a result of the action of physostigmine, proserine, DEP and TEPP was also observed by Landgren et al. (1952). Paskov (1959) demonstrated the same effect produced by the alkaloid galantamine (nivaline), which has a powerful anticholinesterase action. Atanakovich (1950, 1951) observed sensitization of the carotid chemoreceptors to acetylcholine produced by tetramethoquinine methiodide, a preparation with strong anticholinesterase activity. All these findings indicate that anti-cholinesterases intensify the effect of acetylcholine on the carotid bodies and afford evidence that acetylcholine passing through the vascular network in the carotid bodies, even when perfused with Ringer–Locke solution, and so in the absence of blood, is hydro-lysed by cholinesterase. This points to the presence of cholin-esterases in the tissues of the carotid body.

Hollinshead and Sawyer (1945) demonstrated the presence of cholinesterase in the carotid bodies of the cat by direct estimation. Their experiments indicated that the cholinesterase present in the tissues of the carotid bodies was mainly pseudocholinesterase. Koelle (1950, 1951) also studied the cholinesterase activity of the carotid body tissues by chemical methods and also found that the carotid bodies mainly contained pseudocholinesterase. This has been confirmed by experiments in which the carotid chemo-receptors were exposed to one of the substances depressing pseudocholinesterase selectively. One such substance is N-*p*-chlorphenyl-N-methylcarbamate of *m*-hydroxyphenyltrimethyl-ammonium. Experiments carried out in Heymans' laboratory (Casier and Vleschhouwer, 1952) showed that this substance increases the acetylcholine sensitivity of the carotid chemo-receptors considerably.

The presence of cholinesterase in the carotid body supports the view that acetylcholine or other closely related complex esters are concerned in the physiological activity of these bodies. On the other hand, the predominance of pseudocholinesterase would tend to indicate that complex esters other than acetylcholine may be of importance in the specific metabolism of the carotid body tissues.

The experiments of Polyakov-Stanevich (1938a), in which the isolated sinus was perfused in decerebrate cats, revealed that physostigmine 1:100,000 had an excitatory effect on the chemo-receptors as well as increasing their sensitivity to acetylcholine. This effect was, however, inconstant and varied in degree in the experiments on different animals, often being completely absent. A concentration of an anticholinesterase which is sufficient to block cholinesterase does not, therefore, have any significant direct action on the carotid chemoreceptors; the physostigmine effect obviously depends on the presence or absence of acetyl-choline or complex esters with similar action in the carotid bodies. We know that powerful anticholinesterases have a cholinomimetic effect on organs such as the intestine, the tissues of which always contain a certain quantity of acetylcholine. The inconstancy and variation in the intensity of the effect of physostigmine on the carotid bodies is indicative of the inconstant presence of acetylcholine. When endogenous acetylcholine is present in the glomus tissue at the time of physostigmine action, its stabilization has the effect of producing chemoreceptor excitation; in the absence of acetylcholine no such effect will be observed. No direct estimations of acetylcholine in the carotid bodies have so far been made.

Other authors have since studied the direct effect of various anticholinesterases on the carotid chemoreceptors. The results of these investigations differ in different experiments in the same way as those obtained by Polyakov-Stanevich.

Heymans et al. (1953) injected physostigmine and prostigmine into the tissue surrounding the carotid bodies in dogs and observed only very slight respiratory excitation. On the other hand, investigators working in the laboratory of Liljestrand observed various anticholinesterase preparations to have powerful stimulating effects on the carotid chemoreceptors (Liljestrand, 1951; Landgren et al., 1952). Working with cats anaesthetized with urethane or chloralose, these authors injected the substances to be tested into the common carotid artery through a cannula introduced into the thyroid artery and recorded action potentials in Hering's nerve. They found that physostigmine, prostigmine, DFP and TEPP engendered considerable intensification of the fast potentials characteristic of chemoreceptor excitation. Heymans and his co-workers failed to observe any significant effect from the action of anticholinesterases on carotid chemoreceptors and he regarded this as evidence against acetylcholine having any physiological role in the functioning of the carotid bodies; the Swedish authors observed excitation of carotid receptors as a result of the action of anticholinesterases and regarded this fact as in favour of the view that acetylcholine is concerned in the formation of impulses arising in the chemoreceptors.

Without exception, all authors who have studied the effect of anticholinesterases on the sensitivity of the carotid bodies to nicotine, lobeline and other N-cholinomimetic substances not subject to enzymic hydrolysis come to the conclusion that the sensitivity of the carotid bodies is not significantly increased by anticholinesterases. Heymans *et al.* (1953) observed merely slight intensification of the excitatory effect of lobeline after injection of physostigmine or prostigmine into the cellular tissue surrounding the sinus. When, in the experiments of Heymans and his co-workers, physostigmine was injected into the blood no increase was observed in the sensitivity of the carotid bodies to lobeline (Heymans *et al.*, 1944).

In Atanakovich's experiments (1951) the anticholinesterase preparation tetramethochinine methiodide, which intensified the action of acetylcholine on the carotid bodies markedly, did not intensify the effect of nicotine or lobeline on these bodies. In the experiments carried out in Liljestrand's laboratory (Liljestrand, 1952; Landgren *et al.*, 1952) physostigmine and TEPP sometimes even reduced the sensitivity of the carotid bodies to lobeline. A certain degree of change in the sensitivity of carotid chemo-receptors to nicotine and lobeline may be explained by the fact that cholinesterase inhibitors, in addition to inhibiting cholin-esterase, may have a slight direct action on cholinoreactive systems. Evidence of the effect of anticholinesterases on the sensitivity of the carotid bodies to their natural stimuli, oxygen deficiency and excess of carbon dioxide, is of great theoretical importance in the study of the physiological role of acetylcholine in the functioning of chemoreceptors. The results obtained by different authors on this question, however, are very much at variance.

Asratyan (1938c) studied the effect of physostigmine on the sensitivity of the carotid chemoreceptors to potassium cyanide and to carbon dioxide in experiments on decerebrate cats in which the isolated carotid sinus was perfused. The index of chemo-receptor reaction was respiratory excitation. He found that physostigmine salicylate 1:200,000 produced virtually no change in the reaction of the carotid chemoreceptors to carbon dioxide, to reduction in the pH of the Ringer–Locke solution (5·4) or to cyanide (1:5000). Verbeke (1949a, 1949b) obtained similar results in Heymans' laboratory in acute experiments on dogs. The cholinesterase inhibitors which he used were di-isopropylfluoro-phosphate and tetraethylpyrophosphate, and his hypoxia-pro-ducing agent was potassium cyanide. Verbeke concluded that the anticholinesterases did not increase the sensitivity of the chemo-receptors to hypoxia.

Working in the same laboratory, Atanakovich (1950, 1951) examined the anticholinesterase preparation, tetrametochinine methiodide, and found that it did not increase the sensitivity of the carotid sinuses to potassium cyanide or to sodium sulphide. Nor did the dimethylcarbamate of (2-hydroxy-5-phenylbenzyl)-trimethylammonium (No. 683), a very active anticholinesterase, increase the sensitivity of the carotid bodies to the anoxia-producing effect of sodium sulphide (Caldeiro and Garcia Austt, 1949; Mazella and Migliaro, 1949; Fernandez, 1949). These findings constitute one of the reasons why the Heymans School and our own group cannot recognize acetylcholine as the mediator in the excitation of the carotid bodies caused by hypoxia or hypercapnia. If, indeed, active acetylcholine, transmitting excitation to afferent nerves, were liberated in the cells of the carotid bodies in response to oxygen deficiency or to the effects of carbon dioxide, anti-cholinesterases would inevitably have a considerable and very constant intensifying effect on the sensitivity of the carotid chemoreceptors to these physiological stimuli.

The literature, it is true, contains reports of an increase in the sensitivity of the carotid bodies to hypoxia as a result of the action of cholinesterase inhibitors. Such results have mainly been obtained by Liljestrand et al. (1952). Excitation of the carotid chemoreceptors was recorded oscillographically from Hering's nerve in cats narcotized with chloralose or urethane. The substances to be tested were always injected in the same volume and at the same rate (1 ml Ringer's solution in 5 sec) into the carotid artery through a cannula introduced through the thyroid artery. Oxygen deficiency was produced by the breathing of nitrogen containing $5 \cdot 2 – 5 \cdot 6 \%$ oxygen. The anticholinesterases used were eserine (from 50 to 500 γ), prostigmine (250 γ) and DFP (100 γ– 5 mg).

The injection of comparatively small doses of eserine (100 γ) produced an increase of electrical activity in the nerve after 7 sec and maximum activity was reached after 20 sec; the level of activity then attained corresponded to that observed in the nerve during the breathing of a gas mixture containing $5 \cdot 6 \%$ oxygen without any eserine. Chemoreceptor excitation was also observed when the same dose of eserine was injected during the breathing of pure oxygen. The injection of eserine when the animal was breathing a mixture deficient in oxygen (5·2% oxygen) (i.e. when there was excitation) produced a very slight effect. Eserine 500 γ, injected when the animal was breathing oxygen, produced an even greater increase of the electrical activity in the nerve fibres from the carotid chemoreceptors. Eserine (100 γ), had a greater effect on the electrical activity in Hering's nerve when it was injected into a carotid artery when the latter was compressed proximal to the site of the injection. The purpose of the compression was to prolong the time during which eserine was passing through the vessels of the carotid body. When the eserine effect developed, the animal was immediately transferred to breathe a mixture poor in oxygen (5·6% oxygen), which produced a still greater increase in the size of the nerve potentials. On the other hand, the injection of 500 γ eserine into a carotid artery when it was compressed led to complete arrest of the electrical activity in the nerve.

DFP was likewise injected into the blood in the carotid artery; 5 min after the injection of 100 γ the breathing of a gas mixture containing 5·2% oxygen intensified the excitation of the chemoreceptors. The injection of 200 γ TEPP with the carotid artery compressed during the breathing of oxygen led to a considerable but transient increase of electrical activity in the sinus nerve. After 10 min the breathing of a mixture containing 5·6% oxygen produced a further increase of electrical activity. Later, a still larger dose (1 mg) was injected during the breathing of oxygen and still more intense activity was observed in the nerve fibres, but this was not increased further by the breathing of a mixture poor in oxygen. A further increase in the dose of TEPP (5 mg) led to complete arrest of the electrical activity in the sinus nerve.

The authors' special experiments on taste receptors in the lingual mucosa of the frog showed that these high TEPP concentrations produced anaesthesia.

The increase by anticholinesterases in the sensitivity of the carotid bodies to oxygen deficiency, as observed by these authors, is regarded by them as telling evidence in favour of the theory put forward by Schweitzer and Wright (1938) that acetylcholine is the transmitter of the excitation produced in the carotid bodies by hypoxia and carbon dioxide. Developing Schweitzer and Wright's theory, Liljestrand (1954) suggests that the immediate cause of the accumulation of acetylcholine in the carotid bodies during exposure to carbon dioxide and in oxygen deficiency is a shift in the pH of the glomus tissue towards the acid side, which renders the hydrolysis of acetylcholine difficult.

The different results obtained for the influence of anticholinesterases on the sensitivity of the carotid bodies to oxygen deficiency thus led the various authors who have studied this question to diametrically opposite conclusions on the role of acetylcholine in the transmission of impulses in the carotid bodies. A possible assumption is that such very different results, obtained in different laboratories, were due to differences in the methods employed.

Those authors, who used hypoxia-producing poisons (cyanides or sulphides) injected directly into the stream of fluid or blood bathing the sinus in order to test the sensitivity of the carotid bodies to hypoxia, found that eserine, prostigmine and organophosphate anticholinesterases did not produce any significant changes in the sensitivity to hypoxia. The index of carotid chemoreceptor excitation used by these authors was the respiratory reflex.

Liljestrand and his co-workers produced hypoxia by the breathing of a gas mixture poor in oxygen. In their more recent investigations the Swedish authors estimated the carotid chemoreceptor excitation from the electrical activity in the sinus nerve. They concluded from their experiments that anticholinesterases increased the sensitivity of the carotid bodies to hypoxia.

It may seem at first sight that the method employed by the Swedish authors has certain advantages: they employed a more physiological and, therefore, more adequate method of producing hypoxia in the carotid bodies; again, the method of recording chemoreceptor excitation in the immediate vicinity of the site of its development is more accurate. But the breathing of a gas mixture poor in oxygen or rich in carbon dioxide by the animal produces hypoxia and acidosis not only in the tissues of the carotid bodies but in the body generally, and this may lead to liberation of the mediator acetylcholine in other tissues as well as in the carotid bodies. Under these circumstances the presence of cholinesterase inhibitors in the sinus may lead to a considerable increase in the sensitivity of the glomus to the acetylcholine reaching the blood from other tissues. Such action on the carotid bodies of acetylcholine reaching the blood from the body tissues is the more probable in the conditions of Liljestrand's experiments in that, as he himself noted, the doses of anticholinesterase employed produced distant effects as well as the local effect. As a result of this effect acetylcholine released as a mediator in various tissues may have been stabilized and so have reached the general circulation. The increase of electrical activity in the sinus nerve observed by the Swedish authors may possibly be explained by sensitization of the carotid bodies to the acetylcholine appearing in the blood in hypoxaemia.

In any case, the discrepancy between the results obtained by different investigators makes it impossible to state categorically whether or not constant and sustained increase of carotid body sensitivity to hypoxia results from the action of cholinesterase inhibitors. The possible role of acetylcholine as the chemical transmitter of impulses in the carotid bodies likewise remains an open question.

Proof that acetylcholine has this role requires more definite evidence on the effect of anticholinesterases on the physiological function of the carotid bodies and also direct proof that acetylcholine is formed in these bodies during their physiological excitation. Such evidence is not yet available.

At one period Polyakov-Stanevich (1938c) concerned himself with this problem in our laboratory. In some experiments he demonstrated acetylcholine by biological tests in the perfusate flowing from the isolated sinus of the cat through a cannula inserted into the external carotid artery; it was uncertain, however, whether this acetylcholine was secreted by the tissues of the carotid body or by the arterial wall and whether secretion was increased during chemoreceptor excitation. A more accurate examination of this question would require that acetylcholine should be estimated in the blood or perfusate coming from the actual vein of the carotid body. No experiment of this kind has, however, so far been described.

ADRENALINE, NORADRENALINE AND OTHER SYMPATHOMIMETIC AMINES

Kuznetsov (1938) investigated the action of adrenaline on the carotid bodies in experiments on decerebrate cats in which the isolated carotid sinus was perfused. When a 1:100,000 solution of adrenaline (commercial preparation containing noradrenaline as well as adrenaline) was passed through the isolated sinus, there was reflex respiratory excitation and, with this, reduction of blood pressure. Adrenaline in a dilution of 1:1 million, a concentration that has a powerful effect on organs selectively sensitive to the amine, it produced only slight excitation of the carotid receptors in rare instances. This indicates that the carotid bodies have a relatively low sensitivity to sympathomimetic substances.

The low sensitivity of the carotid bodies to adrenaline has been confirmed by Belen'kii (1948a), in whose experiments perfusion of the isolated sinus in the decerebrate cat with a 1:10 million adrenaline solution failed to produce any respiratory changes and a dilution of 1:1 million led to reflex excitation of respiration in only some of the experiments. There can be no doubt that these relatively high adrenaline concentrations, which produce reactions in the carotid receptors, also affect the circulation in the carotid bodies. In his paper Kuznetsov expressed the view that the reflex respiratory excitation produced by adrenaline passing through the isolated sinus was the result of vascular spasm and resultant hypoxia.

The influence of adrenaline on the circulation in the carotid bodies was conclusively demonstrated by the direct experiments of De Castro (1951). Observing the blood flow in the carotid body of the cat under the microscope ($100\times$), he found that the intravenous injection of 1·2 mg adrenaline increased the volume of the carotid body and slowed the flow in its vascular network. In his opinion, these changes depended on contraction of the muscular elements in the arteriovenous anastomoses of the vascular network in the carotid body. Constriction of the anastomoses slowed the blood flow and, by filling the capillaries, led to increase in the volume of the carotid body.

While the respiratory excitation associated with the passage of adrenaline solutions through the isolated sinus can be explained by the direct action of adrenaline on the chemoreceptors or by its action on the vascular network of the carotid body, the associated fall of the general blood pressure observed by Kuznetsov cannot readily be regarded as a reflex developing from the chemoreceptors. Substances which stimulate the carotid chemoreceptors are known to produce a reflex rise of blood pressure.

A depressor effect is known to be produced by the excitation of baroreceptors.

Heymans and his co-workers (1952, 1953, 1955) have proved that local action of adrenaline, noradrenaline and other vasoconstrictor substances on the carotid sinus causes excitation of the baroreceptors located in the sinus walls in the same way as occurs in response to increase of pressure within the sinus. There is simultaneous increase of baroreceptor sensitivity to increase of blood pressure.

The effect of vasoconstrictor substances on the sinus baroreceptors is bound up with the question of the immediate cause of the baroreceptor reaction to pressure change. Hauss *et al.* (1949) have already shown that if stretching of the sinus is prevented by the application of an encircling band, increase of pressure within the sinus does not cause the usual vascular and cardiac reflex. The baroreceptors apparently react to the deformation produced by stretching of the sinus wall and not to pressure change. Deformation may be produced by pharmacological agents with vasoconstrictor action, such as adrenaline, noradrenaline and vasopressin, as well as by the pressure of the blood or mechanical stretching of the artery.

Conversely, vasodilator substances (sodium nitrite, papaverine, priscol), applied locally to the carotid sinus, produce the opposite effect—a fall of blood pressure (Heymans and Neil, 1958).

Final proof that the action of strong adrenaline solutions on the carotid sinuses leads to excitation of baroreceptors was obtained by Landgren *et al.* (1952) in experiments in which they recorded the electrical activity in the sinus nerve. They showed that the action of adrenaline, noradrenaline or vasopressin on the sinus ed to sharp increase of electrical activity in the baroreceptor ibres of Hering's nerve. Similar results have been obtained by Vitzleb (1953).

The authors who have had the greatest share in demonstrating

the reactions of baroreceptors to adrenaline and other vasoconstrictor substances (Heymans and Neil, 1958) emphasize that this
is specifically a matter of the action of very strong solutions of
these substances and that such a reaction can hardly be expected to
develop in the walls of the sinus and the baroreceptors therein
as a result of the action of ordinary doses of adrenaline or noradrenaline after absorption.

Kuznetsov found that the reflexes arising from the action of
adrenaline on the sinus could be abolished by the sympatholytic
substance, ergotoxine. This has been confirmed by many investigators who have observed the abolition of sinus reflexes
arising as a result of the action of adrenaline or noradrenaline by
adrenolytic and sympatholytic preparations such as Dibenamine,
N-(2-bromethyl)-N-ethyl-1-naphthalene-methylamine and Regi-
tine. The existence of this antagonism indicates that, despite the
relatively weak effects of adrenaline and noradrenaline on the
carotid sinus, the effect is nevertheless the result of action on
specific adrenoreactive systems in the carotid sinus region (Heymans et al., 1951; Delaunois and Martini, 1951; Martini and
Rovati, 1954).

While the carotid reflexes to adrenaline only develop in response
to the action of high concentrations, much lower concentrations
can increase the sensitivity of the carotid chemoreceptors to other
stimuli. Belen'kii (1948a) has observed that adrenaline 1:10
million increases the sensitivity of the isolated carotid sinus to
cyanides and to acetylcholine. On the other hand, adrenaline in
a strength of 1:1 million reduces this sensitivity. Belen'kii suggested that this effect of adrenaline on the sensitivity of the
carotid bodies is consistent with sympathetic control of the
carotid receptors.

The sympathetic control of the baroreceptors in the carotid
sinuses has been demonstrated experimentally by Orbeli and
Mikhel'son (1937). The possibility that the changes in the
chemical sensitivity of the carotid bodies produced by adrenaline
are dependent on its effect on the blood supply to these organs
cannot, of course, be excluded.

The carotid chemoreceptors show rather low sensitivity to
other sympathomimetic amines as well as adrenaline. Testing the
effect of sympatol (vasoton) on the isolated sinus of the decere-

brate cat, Kuznetsov (1938) observed reflex respiratory excitation only when the strength of the sympatol solution passed through the sinus was 1:1000. The carotid receptors also reacted feebly to certain other sympathomimetic amines tested by Kuznetsov (tyramine, tetrahydronaphthylamine and ephedrine).

Ephedrine and certain other amines which are close to it in structure (phenamine, etc.) are known to be capable of inhibiting mono-aminoxidase, and this might explain their potentiating effect on the action of adrenaline and noradrenaline.

Mitrofanov (1957) made a special study of the effect of ephedrine on the chemoreceptors of the carotid sinus in our laboratory. He found that ephedrine had only a feeble direct effect on the chemoreceptors and perfusion of the isolated sinus in the decerebrate cat merely produced a slight and inconstant effect: respiration was sometimes stimulated, sometimes depressed. Ephedrine produced a more important change in the sensitivity of the chemoreceptors to other stimuli. In all the dilutions tested (1:16,000, 1:50,000, 1:500,000) ephedrine reduced the sensitivity of the carotid bodies to acetylcholine, and in the presence of 1:10,000 ephedrine, acetylcholine (0·4 ml of a 1:25,000 solution), completely failed to produce the usual reflex respiratory excitation. Ephedrine also intensified the block of carotid body sensitivity to acetylcholine produced by Paramion. At the same time ephedrine increased the sensitivity of the carotid bodies to cyanide.

The different effects of ephedrine on the sensitivity of the carotid bodies to acetylcholine and their sensitivity to cyanide cannot be ascribed to changes in the lumen of the vessels in the carotid body. Obviously, ephedrine has a direct effect on the sensitivity of chemoreceptors. Mitrofanov studied the effect of ephedrine on the cholinoreactive systems in various synapses, both peripheral and central, as well as on the carotid chemoreceptors. He found that ephedrine could reduce both the intensity and duration of the blocking effect of various cholinolytics on cholinergic synapses. Mitrofanov's experiments indicated that the basis of this antagonism was the ability of ephedrine to increase the secretion of acetylcholine by preganglionic fibres during excitation. The sensitivity of the postsynaptic reactive systems to actylcholine was not increased by ephedrine. These findings, in conjunction with the results obtained in investigations on the effect of ephedrine on the sensitivity of the carotid bodies to acetyl-choline and to cyanide, support the view that acetylcholine is the mediator in hypoxic excitation.

An analogy can actually be observed between the effect of ephedrine on ganglionic synapses, in which it promotes the release of acetylcholine and thus facilitates the conduction of impulses over the synapses, and its action on the carotid bodies in which it promotes their excitation by a hypoxic agent. From the standpoint of those authors who consider acetylcholine the mediator in the carotid bodies, being released by its cells and exciting the endings of the sinus nerve, the ephedrine effect can be explained as intensified secretion of acetylcholine as the mediator.

The effect of ephedrine on the sensitivity of the carotid bodies can, however, be given a different interpretation, based on the results obtained by Mitrofanov in his analysis of the effect of ephedrine on ganglionic synapses. This author showed that ephedrine, acting on ganglionic synapses during the transmission of excitation, increases the lability of postsynaptic structures and leads to changes in phosphate metabolism with reduction in the content of inorganic phosphate. It is quite possible that ephedrine may have, in addition to its anti-aminoxidase effect, an influence on other aspects of tissue metabolism, which may explain the increase it produces in the sensitivity of the carotid chemo-receptors to hypoxic poisons.

The effects of certain sympathomimetic amines on the carotid chemoreceptors was investigated by Byck (1957). His experiments, in which the substances were injected into the dog's carotid artery under morphine-chloralose anaesthesia, revealed that methyl, dimethyl and trimethyl derivatives of phenylethylamine, tyramine, 3-hydroxytyramine and noradrenaline produced reflex respiratory excitation more or less in proportion to the strength of their nicotine-like action on the rabbit small intestine.

CHAPTER III

Other Groups of Pharmacological Agents

ALKALOIDS OF THE VERATRINE GROUP

Veratrine is a mixture of alkaloids obtained from the "seeds" of the South American plant *Schoenocaulon officinale*, also called *Sabadilla officinarum*. The individual alkaloids contained in veratrine, veratridine and cevadine, are complex esters of polycyclic tertiary amines.

Close to these in pharmacological properties are certain alkaloids contained in hellebores, *Veratrum album* (Europe) and *Veratrum viride* (North America). The alkaloids with "veratrine effect" which have been most studied are protoveratrine and hermetrine.

The alkaloids contained in veratrine, as well as protoveratrine and hellebore preparations, have attracted special attention during the last few decades because of their successful use as hypotensive agents. It has been established that reflexes from proprioreceptors in the heart, lungs and other receptor zones play a decisive part in the mechanism of their hypotensive effect (Krayer, 1958).

There have also been numerous investigations on the effect of the alkaloids of the veratrine group on the carotid receptors.

These investigations have established that the main alkaloid of veratrine, veratridine, the alkaloid of hellebore, protoveratrine, and also a neogalenical preparation from green hellebore, veriloid, excite the carotid receptors.

This was demonstrated by the reflex reactions of respiration and blood pressure which developed when these alkaloids were made to act directly on the carotid sinuses and also by the increase of electrical activity in the sinus nerves.

The stimulating effect of alkaloids with "veratrine" properties on the carotid chemoreceptors has been recognized by all authors who have investigated the subject.

The most convincing findings are those given in the paper of

Heymans and Vleeschhouver (1950) describing their experiments on dogs.

They showed that the respiratory excitation and bradycardia produced by veratridine are essentially the result of reflexes from the carotid chemoreceptors. The stimulating effect of veratrine on the carotid chemoreceptors has also been demonstrated by Aviado *et al.* (1949).

Belen'kii and Vitolinya (1954) studied the action of veratrine on the carotid chemoreceptors in experiments on decerebrate cats with the carotid sinus isolated. The isolated sinus was perfused with veratrine solutions 1:100,000 to 1:50,000, or 0·4 ml of a 1:5000 solution was injected into the perfusing fluid by means of a syringe. Acting on the isolated sinus, veratrine produced reflex respiratory excitation in six of twelve experiments, the excitation being very pronounced in four. There was at the same time very definite increase in the sensitivity of the chemoreceptors to acetylcholine; their sensitivity to cyanide was unchanged (Fig. 13).

Belen'kii and Vitolinya failed to observe any changes in the depressor reaction to acetylcholine as a result of the intravenous injection of veratrine (1·5–1·0 ml of solution of 1:50,000) in experiments in which they recorded the blood pressure in decerebrate cats. When, however, the animal had been atropinized, veratrine considerably intensified the pressor responses both to acetylcholine and to carbaminoylcholine (Fig. 14). The authors concluded from these experiments that veratrine increases the sensitivity of N-cholinoreactive systems in the carotid bodies.

Because of the practical importance of the hypotensive effect of veratrine preparations, particular attention has been given to the effect of various alkaloids of the veratrine group on the carotid baroreceptors.

Excitation of the carotid baroreceptors is known to produce hypotension whereas excitation of carotid chemoreceptors leads to reflex increase of blood pressure.

Krayer, who has carried out the most complete and comprehensive investigations on the pharmacology of veratrine alkaloids, considers that reflexes from carotid baroreceptors, along with reflexes from other zones, are concerned in the hypotensive effect of these alkaloids (Krayer and Acheson, 1946).

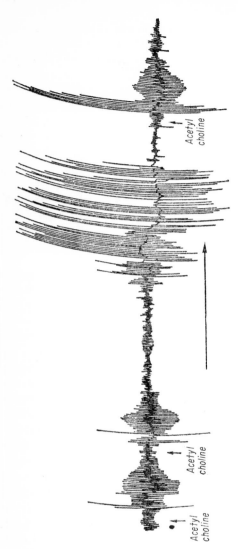

Fig. 13. Decerebrate cat. Perfusion of the isolated carotid sinus. Recording of respiration. The arrows pointing upwards indicate the injection into the perfusing fluid of 0·4 ml of acetylcholine solution (1/10,000). The horizontal arrow indicates the commencement of perfusion with veratrine solution (1/50,000).

To sum up the available evidence, it may be concluded that alkaloids of the veratrine group, which typically excite all sensory endings, excite both chemoreceptors and baroreceptors in the carotid sinuses to some degree.

PAPAVERINE

The mechanism of the stimulating effect of papaverine on respiration has been studied by Macht (1917), Mercier and Delphaut (1934) and by Nims *et al.* (1953). Macht concluded from

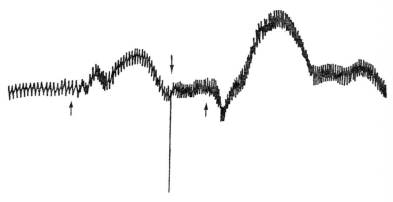

FIG. 14. Decerebrate cat (3·1 kg). A preliminary intravenous injection of 3 ml 1% atropine sulphate solution had been given. Arrows pointing upwards indicate the intravenous injection of 0·2 ml carbocholine solution (1/1000). The arrow pointing downwards indicates the intravenous injection of 1 ml of veratrine solution (1/5000).

his experiments with the "isolated head" that papaverine stimulates respiration by acting directly on the respiratory centre. The conditions of his experiments do not, however, exclude the possibility that papaverine has a reflex effect from the carotid bodies, the chemical sensitivity of which was unknown at the time.

Mercier and Delphaut (1934) observed respiratory excitation when papaverine was injected into animals with the carotid sinuses removed. They considered that this proved the central action of papaverine on respiration. Enders and Schmidt (1952) came to the same conclusion.

Nims *et al.* (1953) came to a different conclusion. Their experiments were carried out on cats and dogs anaesthetized with chloralose. A papaverine solution (20 mg in 1 ml) was injected into the auricular appendage of the right atrium or into the common carotid artery (0·25 ml or more). A respiratory excitation was then observed but this was generally absent when the carotid sinus had been denervated or treated with procaine. Division of the fibres in the sinus nerve supplying the baroreceptors in the sinuses did not prevent the papaverine effect on respiration. Despite denervation of the sinuses, slight respiratory excitation was observed in some experiments in which the papaverine solution was injected into the right auricular appendage of the atrium. This effect was caused by the excitation of aortic chemoreceptors as it disappeared completely when the vagus nerves were divided.

According to these authors, the papaverine effect on the carotid chemoreceptors differs from that of lobeline in having a longer latent period and being more variable, particularly in the case of repeated action. Like the cyanide effect and unlike that of lobeline, the effect of papaverine on the carotid chemoreceptors is not prevented by hexamethonium (6 mg hexamethonium in 3 ml saline injected into a common carotid artery).

ALKALOIDS DERIVED FROM XANTHINE

The question of the participation of the carotid chemoreceptors in the effect of caffeine on respiration was raised soon after discovery of the chemical sensitivity of the carotid bodies. Le Messerier (1936) decided against this as he found that caffeine produced the same respiratory stimulation in animals before and after denervation of the carotid sinuses and bilateral vagotomy. Later, Liljestrand and his co-workers (Landgren *et al.*, 1954) turned their attention to the effect of caffeine and other alkaloids of this group on the carotid chemoreceptors. They introduced the test substances through the thyroid artery into the common carotid artery in cats anaesthetized with chloralose and recorded the electrical activity in Hering's nerve. The cats were given artificial respiration with pure oxygen in order to exclude spontaneous activity in the chemoreceptors. Under these experimental conditions the intracarotid injection of 2·8 mg of caffeine sodium benzoate led to considerable excitation of the carotid chemoreceptors.

In some experiments the internal carotid, the occipital, pharyngeal and lingual arteries and also the small cervical venules discharging into the jugular vein, with the exception of the veins from the carotid body, were tied in order to intensify the effects of the substances introduced on the carotid bodies and to create constant circulatory conditions in them.

A clamp was applied to the common carotid artery before a substance was injected and was removed several seconds after the injection. Under these conditions the injection of caffeine 1·8 mg produced quite distinct chemoreceptor excitation. Theophylline 1·5 mg and theobromine 1 mg had weaker effects. The authors concluded from their experiments that the actions of alkaloids of the xanthine series on the carotid chemoreceptors were relatively feeble, and were due to their feeble anti-cholinesterase properties.

POTASSIUM, MAGNESIUM AND AMMONIUM IONS

The undoubted part played by potassium ions in excitatory processes led to examination of their effect on the carotid bodies.

Small doses of potassium chloride were shown to have a stimulating effect on the carotid bodies by Euler (1938). His experiments were carried out on cats anaesthetized with chloralose. Potassium chloride (from 0·02 to 0·1 mg in the form of 0·1–0·2 solution), introduced into the common carotid artery in the immediate neighbourhood of the carotid bodies, led to respiratory stimulation and increase of blood pressure. When larger doses (0·5–2 mg) were injected, the carotid bodies became insensitive to subsequent injections of either potassium chloride or acetylcholine. The injection of the same doses after denervation of the sinuses or their direct injection into the internal carotid artery towards the brain produced a fall of blood pressure and respiratory depression.

The stimulating effect of potassium chloride on the carotid bodies was confirmed by Winder (1939) in experiments on dogs anaesthetized with morphine and chloralose or nembutal. Isotonic potassium chloride solution (0·01–1·0 ml) was injected rapidly into the common carotid artery all branches of which, with the exception of the lingual artery, had been tied. Powerful transient respiratory excitation was then observed. This effect was absent after denervation of the carotid sinus. When the injection of comparatively large doses (1 ml of isotonic potassium chloride solution) was repeated, its stimulating effect disappeared and the carotid bodies lost their sensitivity to potassium cyanide. There was also some respiratory depression similar to that observed after division of the sinus nerve. The excitatory effect of KCl on the carotid chemoreceptors has been confirmed by Krylov in experiments on the completely isolated sinus (see Fig. 11).

The effects of comparatively large doses of potassium chloride on the carotid chemoreceptors have been studied by Hauss and Shen (1939). Potassium chloride solution was injected into the "carotid sinus sac", prepared as described by Moiseyev, that is into the common carotid artery all branches of which in the sinus region had been divided, in experiments on dogs anaesthetized with chloralose and morphine. An injection of small doses (up to 10 mg) of potassium chloride had no effect of any kind; that of 10 mg in the form of a 1% potassium chloride solution led to respiratory arrest and fall of blood pressure. This reaction was absent after the vessels of the carotid body had been embolized with lycopodium and after division of the sinus nerve. It follows, therefore, that this effect depended on the action of potassium ions on the carotid chemoreceptors.

The effect of magnesium ions on the carotid chemoreceptors has been studied by Anichkov and Tomilina (1950). These experiments were carried out on decerebrate cats, the isolated sinus being perfused in the usual manner. Perfusion of the sinus with 0·2% magnesium chloride solution had no appreciable effect on respiration but had a considerable effect on the sensitivity of the carotid receptors to substances stimulating them. After the isolated sinus had been perfused with magnesium chloride for 20–120 min, acetylcholine (1/5000–20,000), nicotine (1/20,000–1/40,000) and potassium cyanide (1/10,000–1/20,000) either acted feebly or failed entirely to produce the usual effect. All these substances were injected into the stream of perfusion fluid in quantities of 0·4 ml. These various substances in the doses tested produced powerful respiratory excitation before exposure to the action of magnesium chloride. After the carotid sinus had been flushed with Ringer–Locke solution, the chemical sensitivity of its receptors was restored in most experiments. Magnesium ions thus had the effect of abolishing the sensitivity of the chemoreceptors to anoxic poisons and to N-cholinomimetic agents. The sensitivities to nicotine and to cyanide respectively disappeared in different order in different experiments: in some cases the reaction to nicotine was still present when the chemoreceptor reaction to cyanide had disappeared, but sometimes sensitivity to nicotine was first suppressed. The reaction to acetylcholine generally persisted longer than the reaction to nicotine. The suppression of all forms of carotid chemoreceptor sensitivity by magnesium ions distinguishes their effect from the effect of N-cholinolytics (hexamethonium, curarine, etc.), which abolish carotid chemoreceptor sensitivity to acetylcholine and nicotine, but not to anoxic poisons.

It must be remembered that the magnesium ion concentrations employed by us have a pronounced action on the excitatory, process in many other structures: they have local anaesthetic, curare-like and gangliolytic actions.

Anichkov (1936) studied the effect of ammonium ions on the carotid chemoreceptors, using the same method of isolated sinus perfusion in decerebrate cats. The isolated sinus was perfused with ammonium chloride solutions of from 0·1 to 1·0%. No reflex respiratory excitation was observed. In some cases respiratory excitation developed when the carotid sinus was being perfused with only Ringer–Locke fluid. That some of the nerve connexions of the isolated sinus were still intact in these experiments was proved by the injection of small doses of nicotine into the perfusing fluid, with the production of the usual reflex respiratory excitation. That ammonium ions have no stimulating action on the carotid chemoreceptors was also confirmed by our experiments in which ammonium chloride was injected intravenously and into the carotid artery in decerebrate cats and dogs under morphine. The respiratory excitation which developed immediately after the intravenous (1 ml of 5–10% solution) and the intra-carotid injection (0·2 ml of 20% solution) of ammonium chloride was equally pronounced before and after denervation of the carotid sinuses.

Ammonium chloride is known to produce acidosis, which develops some time after its injection. This acidosis, like acidosis of any other origin, causes respiratory excitation which is dependent on excitation of the carotid bodies and aortic bodies, and is not observed after their denervation (Winterstein and Gokhan, 1953a, 1953b). This effect is, however, the result of the action of hydrogen ions and not ammonium ions on the chemoreceptors.

NARCOTIC SUBSTANCES

Asratyan and Kuznetsov (1938) made the first investigations on the effect of narcotic substances on the carotid chemoreceptors. They perfused the isolated sinus in decerebrate cats in the manner usually adopted in our laboratory. The isolated sinus was perfused with solutions of chloroform (0·5–1·0%), chloral hydrate (0·5–1·0%), chloralose (0·1–0·5%), ether (0·5–2·0%) and urethane (0·5–1·0%). In these strengths the narcotic substances produced transient excitation of the chemoreceptors which rapidly gave place to complete loss of their excitability. Weaker solutions of the substances had no appreciable effect on the carotid receptors. The actual order of the narcotic concentrations which are effective in action on the carotid receptors is indicative of the low sensitivity of the latter to agents of this kind. The effects of strong narcotic solutions is probably explained by their denaturing effect on the tissue structures of the carotid sinus. The low sensitivity of the carotid chemoreceptors to narcotic substances has also been demonstrated by Liljestrand and his co-workers (Liljestrand, 1953; Landgren et al., 1953, 1954). These authors also found that excitation of the carotid chemoreceptors was produced by strong solutions of these substances acting for short periods. These experiments were carried out on cats under chloralose or urethane. The narcotic substances were injected in small volumes of normal saline (1–4 ml) directly into the carotid artery. Respiration and blood pressure were recorded.

Action potentials in the sinus nerve were recorded in some experiments. The following strengths of the substances tested were found to be effective: chloroform 0·5%; ether 2–7%; acetone 12%; ethyl alcohol 4–12%; propyl alcohol 1–4%; butyl alcohol 1·6%; amyl alcohol 0·8%.

When these substances were injected into a carotid artery, there was a fairly marked but transient increase of blood pressure and respiratory excitation following momentary arrest. The experiments on denervated sinuses showed that the respiratory arrest was not connected with the action of the narcotic substances on the carotid chemoreceptors and was in fact still more marked after denervation.

The increase of blood pressure depended both on chemoreceptor excitation and on the depressing effect of these substances on the baroreceptors, a fact confirmed by electrophysiological analysis. The electrical activity in the fibres of the sinus nerve carrying the impulses from the baroreceptors when the sinus was exposed to the action of narcotic substances was reduced and activity in the fibres carrying impulses from the chemoreceptors was increased. The very slight rise of blood pressure seen when these substances were injected into a carotid artery with the sinus denervated, is regarded as due to their action on the centres or a direct vasoconstrictor action.

The Swedish investigators (Landgren et al., 1954) tested the action on the carotid chemoreceptors of barbiturates (veronal, thiopental and nembutal), solutions of their sodium salts being injected into a common carotid artery in cats in quantities of from 0·5 to 4·0 mg. In these doses the barbiturates merely produced feeble and inconstant excitation of the carotid chemoreceptors.

Thiopental, pentobarbital and also the "convulsive barbiturate", the sodium salt of 5-1, 3-dimethyl-butyl-5-ethyl barbituric acid, were tested by Dontas (1955) as compounds interfering with tissue respiration and oxidative phosphorylation. The experiments were carried out on cats anaesthetized with urethane and chloralose. The test substances, dissolved in 0·5 ml normal saline, were injected directly into the carotid sinus and the electrical activity in the sinus nerve was recorded. The barbiturates tested had different effects on the carotid receptors. Thiopental and pentobarbital (2–10 mg/ml) reduced electrical activity in the sinus nerve but the "convulsive barbiturate" (0·5–2·0 mg/ml) had a stimulating effect.

Liljestrand (1953) suggested that the stimulating effect of narcotic substances on chemoreceptors is connected with their anticholinesterase properties and is due to the accumulation in the carotid bodies of acetylcholine which is here, in the author's opinion, the transmitter of centripetal impulses. Liljestrand and his coworkers (Landgren et al., 1953) tested this theory on the mechanism of the action of narcotic substances on the carotid chemoreceptors. In their experiments the excitatory effect of narcotic substances on the carotid chemoreceptors, recorded electrophysiologically, was abolished by injection into the carotid artery of the cholinolytic substances, atropine sulphate (2 mg), D-tubocurarine (0·3 mg) and hexamethonium (2 mg). The excitation of the carotid chemoreceptors produced by narcotic substances was also abolished by injection into the carotid artery of 1 ml 0·05% ammonia solution.

The authors are of the opinion that their results confirm their theory that anti-cholinesterase action is the cause of the chemoreceptor excitation produced by narcotic substances.

HISTAMINE AND 5-HYDROXYTRYPTAMINE

The effects of the biogenous amines, histamine and 5-hydroxytryptamine (serotonin, 5HT), on the carotid chemoreceptors have been studied in connexion with their possible involvement in the physiological activity of the carotid bodies. The effect of histamine on the carotid chemoreceptors has been studied by Landgren *et al.* (1954), who prepared the sinus in a cat which they had used in caffeine experiments in a way which enabled them to avoid the fall of blood pressure that results from the action of histamine after absorption. Doses of from 2 to 50 γ histamine hydrochloride, injected into the carotid sinus, had no effect of any kind on the electrical activity in the sinus nerve whereas even 2 γ acetylcholine under the same conditions produced chemoreceptor excitation. These results threw doubt on the theory of Fabiani and Szebehelyi (1948) that histamine was concerned in the transmission of excitation in the carotid bodies. The grounds on which this theory was advanced were that their experiments had shown that an antihistaminic preparation, Antistin (2-N-benzylanilinomethyl-Δ^2-imidazoline) prevented the respiratory stimulation produced by the breathing of a gaseous mixture containing 10% oxygen. This preventive effect of antihistaminic substances on the dyspnoea produced by anoxia was not, however, confirmed in Liljestrand's investigations (1949). Landgren *et al.* (1954) likewise found that an antihistaminic preparation, Lergitin (N-benzyl-N, N'-dimethyl-N-phenylethylene-diamine), injected directly into the sinus, reduced the sensitivity of the carotid chemoreceptors only in a dose which had a local anaesthetic effect.

Published reports are available on the effect of 5-hydroxytryptamine on the carotid chemoreceptors. In the experiments of

Douglas and Toh (1952) on dogs, 0·1–10 mg produced respiratory excitation when injected into a common carotid artery with the internal carotid, external carotid and occipital arteries ligatured. In the authors' opinion this excitation was a reflex from the carotid chemoreceptors as it was absent when the sinus nerve had been divided.

Ginzel and Kottegoda (1954) made a more detailed analysis of the action of 5-hydroxytryptamine on carotid receptors. Their experiments were on cats anaesthetized with chloralose or pentobarbital. The drug, contained in 0·1 ml Ringer–Locke solution, was injected into the carotid sinus through a cannula inserted into the lingual artery. The external carotid artery was tied. The injection of 2–6 γ 5-hydroxytryptamine produced respiratory excitation after momentary arrest, associated with a fall of blood pressure.

When the sinus nerve had been divided, only the respiratory arrest developed and there was no respiratory excitation or fall of blood pressure in response to the injection of 5-hydroxytryptamine. The respiratory excitation did not depend on the fall of blood pressure as it developed even when the blood pressure was maintained at constant level artificially.

The authors suggest that the respiratory excitation was the result of a reflex from the carotid chemoreceptors; they consider that spasm of the vessels in the carotid body, produced by 5-hydroxytryptamine, was possibly responsible for this effect. The fall of blood pressure they regard as a reflex from the baroreceptors, excitation of which is produced by the deformation of the sinus wall produced by 5-hydroxytryptamine.

When the injection of 5-hydroxytryptamine was repeated, the reaction from the carotid receptors diminished and disappeared. Hexamethonium in doses preventing acetylcholine and nicotine effects on the carotid receptors had no effect on their sensitivity to 5-hydroxytryptamine. Larger doses of serotinin (50–100 γ), caused the blood pressure to fall whether the injections were made into sinuses with intact nerve supply or into denervated sinuses, this in their opinion being due to the central action of 5-hydroxytryptamine. Heymans and Heuvel-Heymans (1953) studied the effect of large doses of 5-hydroxytryptamine on the carotid sinus in the dog. The dogs were anaesthetized with morphine and chloralose and the 5-hydroxytryptamine was injected into the common carotid artery, the branches of which in the neighbourhood of the sinus had been ligatured. The respiratory excitation and fall of blood pressure then observed developed after a latent period lasting several seconds and was equally pronounced irrespective of whether the sinus nerve was intact or had been divided. The reaction was likewise virtually unchanged by bilateral vagotomy. The authors concluded that the carotid receptors were not concerned in the action of 5-hydroxytryptamine on respiration and blood pressure. Heymans and Neil suggest that some of the differences between authors on the question of the effect of 5-hydroxytryptamine on the carotid receptors can be explained by different degrees of purity of the preparations employed.

CHAPTER IV

Theory of the Mechanism of Chemoreception in the Carotid Bodies

THE various forms of sensitivity of the carotid body chemoreceptors, which react by excitation to the action of a number of physiological stimuli (hypoxia, hypercapnia, acidosis) and pharmacological agents, had made this "organ of chemical sensitivity" interesting material for the investigation of the delicate mechanism whereby the effect of stimulation is transformed into a nerve impulse.

"ACID" AND MEDIATOR THEORIES

As the impulses arising in the chemoreceptors of the carotid body are most clearly seen in reflex respiratory changes, it was naturally thought that the mechanism responsible for the development of impulses in the chemoreceptors was similar to that for the development of impulses in the respiratory centre of the medulla (Bernthal, 1932, 1934, 1938; Winder, 1937; Gesell, 1939; and others). Consequently, the theory of a reduction of the intracellular pH as the immediate cause of the development of excitation in the cells of the respiratory centre was also applied to the chemoreceptor apparatus in the carotid body. This hypothesis would explain the stimulating effect on the chemoreceptors of oxygen lack as well as that of carbon dioxide and other acids.

We know that when cells are subjected to low oxygen pressure, the anaerobic carbohydrate breakdown comes into operation in the cells and this leads to accumulation of lactic acid.

Winder (1937) carried out experiments in an attempt to confirm the "acid" theory of hypoxic excitation of chemoreceptors. He applied to the isolated carotid sinus in dogs narcotized with morphine and urethane a dose of mono-iodoacetate, a substance which inhibits glycolysis and, consequently, prevents the formation of lactic acid. After this treatment perfusion of the sinus with hypoxic blood (containing less than 0·5% oxygen) no longer caused the development of reflex reactions, although when the sinus was perfused with hypercapnic blood (containing 35% carbon dioxide), reflex reactions were observed in most of the experiments.

The experiments of Estrand, Green and Neil, reported by Heymans and Neil (1958), did not confirm Winder's results. Results by Chernigovskii (1947a, 1947b), obtained, it is true, not on the carotid chemoreceptors, but on chemoreceptors in an isolated intestinal loop, likewise differed from those of Winder's experiments. Chernigovskii observed disappearance of the reflex reactions to both hypoxia and carbon dioxide after poisoning of the chemoreceptors with substances inhibiting glycolysis (mono-iodoacetate and sodium fluoride).

If Winder's experiments, which have not been confirmed, are discarded, the only remaining basis for the argument of the supporters of the "acid" theory of excitation in chemoreceptor cells is indirect evidence, which also admits of a different interpretation. Such arguments include the effect of temperature and ischaemia on the activity of the carotid chemoreceptors and the combined action of hypoxia and hypercapnia (Winder et al., 1938a, 1938b; Bernthal and Weeks, 1939; Winder, 1942).

It must be recognized that, although the "acid" theory has attained considerable popularity (see Gesell, 1939; Schmidt and Comroe, 1940; Euler et al., 1939; Ado and Ishimova, 1947; and others), its experimental basis is not by any means solid.

The carotid body chemoreceptor sensitivity to acetylcholine was discovered (Anichkov et al., 1936; Heymans et al., 1936) at a time when the interests of physiologists were firmly fixed on the problem of the chemical mechanism for the transmission of nerve impulses in synapses. The role of acetylcholine as the mediator in the region of the endings of parasympathetic fibres and also in ganglionic and neuromuscular synapses had been discovered by this time. The demonstration of the sensitivity of the carotid chemoreceptors to acetylcholine naturally raised the question of the possible physiological significance of acetylcholine in chemoreceptor function.

The idea that acetylcholine might be of physiological importance in the functioning of the carotid body was first expressed by Anichkov at the 15th International Physiological Congress in the course of the discussion on a paper read by him (Anichkov *et al.*, 1935). Schweitzer and Wright (1938) suggested that acetylcholine is the only immediate stimulus for the chemoreceptor apparatus and that the stimulating effects of all other agents are mediated through acetylcholine. In other words, Schweitzer and Wright ascribed to acetylcholine the same role in the chemoreceptor function of the carotid body that it plays in the paths for the conduction of efferent impulses.

This idea received its most complete development in the research of the Swedish pharmacological school. Euler *et al.* (1939, 1941) developed a theory that acetylcholine is formed in the sensory elements of the carotid body as a result of the action of carbon dioxide and that by means of the acetylcholine the chemical stimulus was transformed into an afferent nerve impulse. These authors recorded the action potentials in the sinus nerve of the cat and observed that the electrical activity produced by hypoxia or carbon dioxide could be abolished by the intravenous injection of ammonia. At the same time the action potentials in response to nicotine, lobeline, acetylcholine or potassium salts were still observed. The conclusion drawn from this was that acetylcholine and the "ganglionic" poisons acted more proximally than hypoxia and carbon dioxide in the chemoreceptor apparatus. The hypothesis derived from this was that both oxygen lack and excess of carbon dioxide led to a shift of the reaction within the chemoreceptor cells towards the acid side and this led to liberation of acetylcholine; the latter acted as a mediator in the ganglionic synapses which presumably must be included in the path for the conduction of impulses from the chemoreceptor cells in the carotid body to the central nervous system. According to this hypothesis, it is on these ganglionic synapses that ganglionic poisons act.

It is quite obvious that the acetylcholine theory for the mechanism of chemoreception in the carotid bodies does not altogether exclude the "acid" theory and, indeed, it accepts and supplements it.

Another variant of the acetylcholine theory (Gesell and Hansen, 1945) is the concept of the constant formation of very small quantities of acetylcholine in the cells of the carotid bodies, the substance being hydrolysed by cholinesterase immediately after its liberation. As acidotic shifts reduce cholinesterase activity and thus potentiate acetylcholine effects, hypoxia, hypercapnia and other agents promoting acidosis lead to accumulation of acetylcholine and thus produce excitation in the chemoreceptor apparatus. This view is supported by Liljestrand (1954).

There is in the chemoreceptor apparatus of the carotid body only one point at which it can be assumed that there is chemical transmission of impulses, namely the point of contact between the chemoreceptor cells and the endings of the sinus nerve which, from the work of De Castro (1926, 1927–1928, 1951), Lavrent'yev (1943), Ross (1959) and a number of other investigators, can be regarded as a synapse.

According to these views, the acetylcholine theory of chemoreception in the carotid body is explained in the following way: hypoxia, hypercapnia and acidosis lead to liberation or accumulation of acetylcholine in chemoreceptor cells; the acetylcholine acts on the endings of the sinus nerve and causes the development of afferent impulses in these endings.

Oxygen lack, carbon dioxide and various acids on the one hand and acetylcholine and N-cholinomimetic agents on the other, act on different successively arranged links in the afferent chain for the development and transmission of chemoreceptor signals.

Ado and his co-workers (see Ado and Ishimova, 1947; Ishimova, 1947, 1948; and others) share the acetylcholine theory of chemoreception in the carotid bodies. Chernigovskii (1943, 1947a, 1947b) also comes to the conclusion that chemical sensitivity to hypoxia and carbon dioxide and chemical sensitivity to acetylcholine has different locations, as a result of his experiments on the chemoreceptors in an isolated intestinal loop.

The acetylcholine theory of the mechanism of chemoreception cannot be rejected on grounds of inconsistency with facts or illogicality. The theory is, however, a matter of debate.

At the same time there is a considerable volume of experimental material against the acetylcholine theory of the mechanism of chemoreception.

If acetylcholine is a mediator in the activity of the carotid bodies, then anticholinesterases should intensify reflex reactions to hypoxia and carbon dioxide as well as those to acetylcholine. However, it has not been established that anticholinesterases have this effect even in the simplest experiments in which the direct physiological reaction to chemoreceptor excitation by anoxic poisons is estimated (Chapter II).

This effect has only been observed by recording potentials in the sinus nerve during periods of general hypoxaemia.

Evidence against the mediator role of acetylcholine in the carotid body is also provided by the results of many experiments on the effect of cholinolytic substances on the carotid bodies (see Chapter II), in which it was shown that ganglion-blocking and curare-like substances abolished the sensitivity of the carotid chemoreceptors to acetylcholine and substances with nicotine-like actions, but that they had little effect on the sensitivity of the receptors to anoxia (Moe *et al.*, 1948; Vedeneyeva, 1951; Douglas, 1952a, 1952c; Douglas and Gray, 1953; Denisenko, 1953; Mitrofanov, 1957).

It is not inappropriate to note here that atropine, perfused through the isolated carotid sinus of the cat, even in a strength of 1:10,000 has no significant effect on the sensitivity of the chemoreceptors to carbon dioxide or cyanide (Asratyan, 1938). Yet, those with concentrations of atropine block the sensitivity of the carotid chemoreceptors to acetylcholine completely (Polyakov-Stanevich, 1938a).

Similar results have been obtained in experiments with nicotine. Perfusion of the isolated sinus with nicotine 1:100,000 for 5–7 min abolished the reaction to acetylcholine and lobeline but did not interfere with chemoreceptor sensitivity for sodium sulphide (Ishimova, 1948).

Asratyan's experiments (1938b), described in Chapter II, show that higher concentrations of nicotine reduce the sensitivity of carotid receptors to acetylcholine and cholinomimetic substances very considerably, but produce little change in the effects of cyanide and CO_2.

Although the results of their experiments with tetraethylammonium were at variance with the acetylcholine theory of the chemoreceptor mechanism, Moe *et al.* (1948) attempted to reconcile their results with this theory. They did this by suggesting that some fibres of the sinus nerve formed synapses with the chemoreceptor cells on the surfaces of these cells ("external" synapses) and other neurofibrils ended within the chemoreceptor cell, forming "internal" synapses, which were not affected by the action of pharmacological agents introduced from the outside. They then suggested that when tetraethylammonium was injected into the animal, only the "external" synapses were blocked as the tetraethylammonium injected into the blood did not reach the "internal" synapses. The subsequent injection of acetylcholine, nicotine or lobeline, which likewise reached only the "external" synapses, did not produce the usual reflex reaction. The chemoreceptors retained their sensitivity to hypoxia and hypercapnia as the acetylcholine liberated within the chemoreceptor cells as a result of these stimuli exercised its effect on the "internal" receptors which had remained unblocked.

There was at the time some morphological basis for such an hypothesis: a number of investigators (Boeke, 1932; Abraham, 1942; De Castro, 1951; De Kock, 1954) had studied the histology of the carotid body and had demonstrated neurofibrils in the protoplasm of chemoreceptor cells, fibrils which presumably constituted the "intracellular synapses". However, the use of electron microscopy for study of the minute structure of the carotid bodies has excluded the existence of "intracellular synapses" and has proved that the contact between sinus nerve neurofibrils and chemoreceptor cells takes place solely on the surface of these cells (Ross, 1959).

The findings of Hollinshead and Sawyer (1945) and Kelly (1950, 1951) that the cells of the carotid body contain mainly pseudocholinesterase and not true cholinesterase constitute further evidence against accepting acetylcholine as the mediator in the carotid bodies.

This has been confirmed by the histochemical investigations of Ross (1957), who believes that there is a chemical mechanism for the transmission of excitation from chemoreceptor cells to afferent nerve endings that suggests that the mediator is not acetylcholine, but some other choline ester.

Although the acetylcholine theory of chemoreception is attractive, it must be admitted that there is more evidence against it than in its favour. Heymans and Neil (1958) have discussed the literature on this question and expressed their conviction that acetylcholine is not concerned in the transmission of chemoreceptor impulses.

Mention may be made of the attempt to put histamine forward as the mediator of chemoreceptor impulses in the carotid body.

However, Landgren *et al.* (1954), who injected histamine into a carotid artery, failed to observe any change in the electrical activity of the sinus nerve or change of any kind in the reaction to hypoxia as a result of the action of antihistaminic substances.

A NEW APPROACH TO THE SUBJECT

Against the views of supporters of the acetylcholine theory of chemoreception, who consider that the sensitivity of the carotid body chemoreceptors to its physiological stimuli and its sensitivity to acetylcholine are located in different links of this apparatus, one of the authors of this book (Anichkov, 1936, 1937) suggested that the chemoreceptor cells constitute the sole morphological substrate of chemical sensitivity in the carotid body. The response of the chemoreceptor cells to different chemical stimuli was linked with the presence in these cells of different biochemical systems capable of reacting to suitable stimuli. In developing this concept, he put forward the hypothesis that there are at least two such reactive biochemical systems in the carotid body, a system providing chemical sensitivity to oxygen lack and another sensitive to acetylcholine and cholinomimetic agents, that is a cholinoreactive system.

The evidence provided by pharmacological analysis of chemoreception in the carotid bodies led to the concept that the reactive system responsible for the sensitivity of the chemoreceptors to oxygen starvation is the "cytochrome–cytochrome oxidase" system (Anichkov, 1945). The cholinoreactive system of the carotid body has been classified as N-cholinoreactive (i.e. nicotine-sensitive) (Anichkov and Grebenkina, 1946; Anichkov, 1951), similar to the cholinoreactive systems of ganglion cells, the chromaffin cells of the adrenal medulla and the end-plates of skeletal muscles.

These views differ fundamentally from those of the upholders of the acetylcholine theory of chemoreception, who locate sensitivities to hypoxia and to acetylcholine respectively in different successive links in the chain responsible for the development and subsequent spread of afferent chemoreceptor signals. According to the new concepts, sensitivities to hypoxia and to acetylcholine are determined by the existence side by side in the chemoreceptor cells of reactive systems with selective sensitivity, each of them the place of origin of the signals for the action of the corresponding stimuli. This approach to an understanding of the mechanism of chemoreception readily explains the possible retention of sensitivity to hypoxia when sensitivity to acetylcholine is lost, a position which the acetylcholine theory fails to explain.

The view that the chemoreceptor cells in the carotid body are the element responsible for its sensitivity to all chemical stimuli finds interesting confirmation in the investigations of De Castro (1951).

In experiments on cats De Castro changed the nature of the afferent innervation of the carotid body. Two operations were performed successively on the animals. The first was to suture the preganglionic sympathetic nerve in the neck to the vagus nerve proximal to the nodose ganglion. The result of this operation was that the preganglionic sympathetic fibres, separated from their cells, underwent degeneration and fibres from the nerve cells in the nodose ganglion of the vagus nerve grew out along their course. Artificial synapses between the sensory fibres of the vagus nerve and sympathetic ganglionic cells were thus formed. Degeneration of the efferent fibres of the vagus nerve was ensured by division of the vagus before its exit from the skull. In the second operation the vagus nerve was sutured below the nodose ganglion with the peripheral segment of the glossopharyngeal nerve at a point between the origin of the sinus nerve and the ganglion petrosum. After this operation the fibres of the sinus nerve, separated from their cells, degenerated and were replaced by fibres growing out from the nerve cells in the nodose ganglion of the vagus nerve.

As a result of these operations the cat had an extremely simple artificial reflex arc not connected with the central nervous system and consisting of only two neurons, a sensory one from a cell in the nodose ganglion and an efferent one from a cell in the superior cervical sympathetic ganglion.

Experiments on the isolated sinus of such cats have established that reflex reactions—dilatation of the pupil, contraction of the nictitating membrane, vasoconstriction in the ear and a pilomotor response—developed in the animals on the side on which the perfusion fluid passing through the sinus was saturated with carbon dioxide, its pH being thus reduced, and also when lobeline was added to the perfusion fluid. Thus, despite a change in the afferent innervation of the carotid body and the creation of new synapses between the chemoreceptor cells and afferent fibres, the sensitivity of the chemoreceptor apparatus to various chemical stimuli (including a cholinomimetic agent—lobeline) was completely retained.

De Castro's experiments afford very convincing evidence that the selective chemical sensitivity of the carotid body depends solely on the specific character of the chemoreceptor cells, and not on the particular functional features of the endings of the sinus nerve.

Our latest investigations on the mechanism of chemoreception have been based on the concept that all forms of chemical sensitivity in the carotid body are located in its chemoreceptor cells. Our approach to this question has varied slightly in the course of the work. Whereas earlier we had suggested that the development of excitation in the chemoreceptor apparatus was a direct result of interaction between the chemical stimulus and the corresponding reactive system of the chemoreceptor cell, we subsequently abandoned this view. The fact is that this approach to the question requires the existence in chemoreceptor cells of a definite set of reactive systems for all the agents which elicit signals from the chemoreceptor apparatus. The emergence and firm establishment of such reactive systems could, of course, only be effected over a long period of animal evolution. This could have occurred in the case of stimuli such as oxygen lack, the action of carbon dioxide and increased hydrogen ion concentration. The existence of cholinoreactive systems in chemoreceptor cells could also be understood when it is considered that these cells originated from sympathogonia, which also give rise to ganglion cells. It is, however, impossible to imagine how reactive systems providing sensitivity to substances absolutely foreign to the body, such as sodium nitrate or 2,4-dinitrophenol, could arise in chemoreceptor cells.

A much more fruitful and likely concept is that it is not the actual fact of reception of a chemical stimulus but the changes which develop in the biochemical processes occurring in chemoreceptor cells as a result of this reception which constitute the immediate cause of the development of excitation in the chemoreceptor apparatus. The investigations described in the following chapters were carried out with this as a working hypothesis.

CHAPTER V

Action of Reducing Agents on the Chemoreceptors of the Carotid Body

THE results of investigations on the effect of reducing agents on the carotid body chemoreceptors (Belen'kii, 1949a) played a decisive part in the formulation of our working hypothesis as explained at the end of the last chapter.

The purpose of these investigations was to determine the role of cytochrome oxidase as a reactive system of the chemoreceptor cells in their reaction to pharmacological agents producing hypoxia. We sought to determine whether inhibition of cytochrome oxidase was the immediate cause of excitation in the chemoreceptors or whether excitation developed as a result of changes in cell metabolism produced by the inhibition of cytochrome oxidase activity.

For this, we determined whether chemoreceptors were sensitive to pharmacological agents that limited the intensity of oxidative processes in the tissues without at the same time affecting cytochrome oxidase activity. Obviously, such agents must include substances with high absolute negative oxidation-reduction potential, i.e. so-called reducing agents.

The effects on the isolated carotid sinus of a number of reducing agents (hydroxylamine, p-aminophenol, hydroquinone, methol, formaldehyde, and $NADH_2$) were studied in decerebrate cats. The reflex reactions were assessed by recording of respiration and, in some experiments, arterial pressure. The substances under examination were injected into the fluid passing through the sinus, in amounts from 0·2 to 2·0 ml.

HYDROXYLAMINE

Hydroxylamine hydrochloride (0·4–20 ml of solutions 1/1,000,000–1/5000) was injected into the fluid perfusing the isolated carotid sinus. The amounts of hydroxylamine administered thus ranged from 2 to 400 γ.

Respiratory stimulation, mainly in the form of an increase in the amplitude of the respiratory movements, followed the introduction of hydroxylamine into the isolated carotid sinus region in all experiments (Fig. 15).

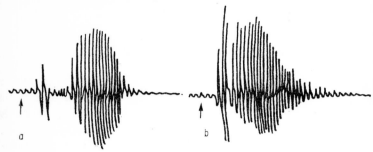

FIG. 15. Decerebrate cat. Perfusion of the isolated carotid sinus. Recording of respiration.
a—reaction to the injection of 40 γ hydroxylamine into the perfusing fluid. b—reaction to the injection of 200 γ *p*-aminophenol. Arrows—injections.

At the commencement of an experiment 40 γ hydroxylamine was usually injected into the perfusing fluid. If distinct respiratory excitation was then observed, the dose was reduced progressively until the threshold was reached. Conversely, if 40 γ hydroxylamine produced no reaction, the amounts were increased gradually until the threshold was reached.

The threshold dose of hydroxylamine was found to vary quite considerably, from 2 γ (in one of eleven experiments) to 200 γ (in two experiments), with an average of 63·8 ± 20·6 γ.

The intensity of the respiratory response to one and the same dose of hydroxylamine also varied very considerably in different animals.

p-AMINOPHENOL

p-Aminophenol sulphate solutions (0·2–2·0 ml of solutions 1/100,000–1/1000) were injected into the fluid passing through the isolated carotid sinus. The quantity introduced ranged from 20 γ to 2 mg.

Acting on the isolated carotid sinus region, *p*-aminophenol, like hydroxylamine, produced respiratory excitation (see Fig. 15).

The threshold dose varied just as widely as with hydroxylamine. It was 20 γ in one, and 2 mg in another, of the eleven experiments. The average threshold dose for eleven experiments was 320 $\pm$ 75·7 γ.

The reactions in the different animals to the same dose of p-aminophenol likewise varied considerably in intensity. Very intense respiratory reactions (with the amplitude increased ten times or more) were seen less frequently with p-aminophenol than with hydroxylamine.

HYDROQUINONE

Hydroquinone was tested in dilutions of from 1/100,000 to 1/100 and in each experiment 2 ml was injected into the fluid passing through the isolated carotid sinus. The amounts of hydroquinone introduced thus ranged from 20 γ to 20 mg.

Hydroquinone, like the two substances previously described, produced respiratory excitation.

The doses of hydroquinone that produced this effect were considerably larger than the corresponding doses of hydroxylamine or p-aminophenol. Also, the animals exhibited a much greater range of variation in individual carotid chemoreceptor sensitivity to hydroquinone. Extreme sensitivity was only noted in one of ten experiments: the threshold dose in this experiment was 20 γ. In another the threshold dose was found to be 20 mg. The average threshold dose in ten experiments was 3·14 $\pm$ 1·91 mg.

The respiratory reactions produced by hydroquinone were much less intense than those following the introduction of hydroxylamine or p-aminophenol.

OTHER REDUCING AGENTS

Some other reducing agents were also tested for their effects on the isolated carotid sinus.

Experiments were carried out with metol (monomethyl-p-aminophenol sulphate), a reducing agent extensively used in photographic laboratory technique. When 200 γ–1 mg metol (solutions 1/10,000–1/500 in a volume of 2 ml) were injected into the fluid passing through the isolated carotid sinus, there was respiratory excitation, as with the reducing agents previously tested. Since aldehydes have reducing powers, formaldehyde was also tested, a 1% formalin solution being injected into the fluid passing through the isolated carotid sinus. Introduced in this way, formaldehyde produced a definite respiratory reaction.

We also investigated the effect on the isolated carotid sinus of an agent which participates as a reducing agent in the biochemical processes for the transfer of hydrogen, mainly the reduced form of nicotinamide—adeninedinucleotide (NADH$_2$). Immediately before an experiment a NAD preparation was dissolved in water and converted into its reduced form by treatment with sodium hyposulphite. The solutions thus obtained, containing from 0·05 to 1·0% NADH$_2$, were injected in quantities of 0·2–2·0 ml into the fluid passing through the isolated carotid sinus. Respiratory excitation was observed as with the other reducing agents tested (Fig. 16).

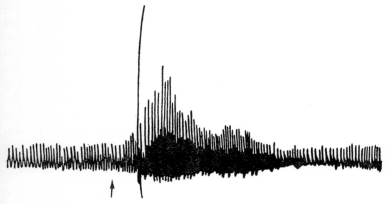

Fig. 16. Decerebrate cat. Perfusion of the isolated carotid sinus. Recording of respiration. Reaction to injection into the perfusing fluid of 2 mg (0·4 ml of 0·5% solution) of the reduced form of diphosphopyridine nucleotide.

Proofs of the Reflex Nature of the Effects of Reducing Agents on Respiration

As there is always a possibility, when solutions are passed through the isolated carotid sinus, that they may enter the blood-stream through small vascular branches which have not been tied, additional experiments were essential to prove the reflex nature of the effects produced by pharmacological agents injected into the fluid passing through the isolated sinus. Such experiments were also carried out with reducing agents, viz. with hydroxylamine, *p*-aminophenol, hydroquinone and metol, and in two different ways.

(1) After a reducing agent had been injected into the stream of the perfusing fluid, the region of the carotid sinus was infiltrated with novocain. Injection of the reducing agent into the perfusion fluid was then repeated.

These experiments showed that treatment of the carotid sinus region with procaine abolished the respiratory reaction to reducing agents completely.

(2) The first rib was resected in the decerebrate cat. The subclavian artery was then approached and all its branches, with the exception of the common carotid and vertebral arteries, were tied. The subclavian artery itself was tied, distal to the origin of these vessels, and a clamp was applied to the artery proximal to this point. A cannula directed against the blood-stream was inserted into the subclavian artery between the ligature and the clamp. A clamp having first been applied to the vertebral artery, the reducing agent to be studied could be injected into the carotid artery by means of a syringe connected to the cannula by rubber tubing. Injected in this way, the substance under investigation reached the carotid body but did not enter the cerebral circulation. If, before injection of the reducing agent, a clamp were applied to the common carotid artery and the vertebral artery was left open, the substance injected reached the central nervous system but not the carotid body.

These experiments revealed that reducing agents only produced respiratory excitation when injected into the carotid artery and had no effect on respiration when injected into the vertebral artery.

These additional experiments confirmed that the respiratory excitation produced by reducing agents is a reflex from carotid body chemoreceptors and showed that these substances had no direct stimulating effect on the respiratory centre.

Relative Activity of Reducing Agents

The experiments on the effects of reducing agents on the carotid sinus chemoreceptors revealed that different reducing agents exhibited different activities as chemoreceptor stimuli. For some of the reducing agents the number of experiments was sufficient to establish the average threshold doses producing respiratory reflexes. As indicated above, these were:

Hydroxylamine	$63 \cdot 8 \pm 20 \cdot 6$ mg
p-Aminophenol	$320 \pm 75 \cdot 7$ mg
Hydroquinone	$3 \cdot 14 \pm 1 \cdot 91$ mg

Despite these quite considerable differences in the average threshold doses for these three reducing agents, the objective assessment of their significance revealed that, statistically, the only significant difference is that between the values for hydroxylamine and p-aminophenol ($t = 3 \cdot 26$; P $< 0 \cdot 01$). The differences between the threshold doses for hydroquinone and p-aminophenol ($t = 1 \cdot 63$; $0 \cdot 25 >$ P $> 0 \cdot 1$) and even between hydroquinone and hydroxylamine ($t = 1 \cdot 77$; $0 \cdot 1 >$ P $> 0 \cdot 05$) proved statistically invalid, on account of the inadequate number of experiments and the exceptionally pronounced variations in the individual sensitivity of the different animals to hydroquinone. At the same time hydroquinone was much inferior to hydroxylamine and p-aminophenol in the intensity of the respiratory reactions which developed when these reducing agents acted on the isolated carotid sinus. This makes it extremely likely that even if the number of experiments were increased, the threshold doses of hydroquinone would differ materially from the threshold doses of the other two reducing agents. Based on the intensity of the respiratory reactions alone, these reducing agents can be arranged in order of diminishing activity thus: hydroxylamine, p-aminophenol, hydroquinone.

One possible suggestion is that the different effects of these reducing agents on chemoreceptors can be explained by differences in the rates of the oxidation–reduction reactions in which they participate.

This possibility was tested in model experiments in which the activities of hydroxylamine, p-aminophenol and hydroquinone as methaemoglobin-formers were compared. Methaemoglobin-formation resulting from the action of reducing agents is a very complex process. Inasmuch as the conversion of haemoglobin to methaemoglobin is an oxidative reaction, reducing agents can effect this process only after preliminary oxidation. The mechanism of the process has been worked out by Heubner (1913) for p-aminophenol as a methaemoglobin-former.

According to Heubner, p-aminophenol is oxidized by oxygen to the quinoneimine; the latter reacts with haemoglobin, which is converted to methaemoglobin and the quinoneimine is itself reduced again to p-aminophenol.

Without entering into a detailed discussion of the mechanism of methaemoglobin formation by reducing agents, we may take it that this reaction is an oxidation–reduction reaction and that it can in consequence give an indication of the rates at which various reducing agents react in biological oxidation–reduction reactions.

The velocities of methaemoglobin formation were compared when equimolecular amounts of hydroxylamine, p-aminophenol and hydroquinone were added to a 3% aqueous solution of haemolysed blood. The formation of methaemoglobin was assessed from the development of an absorption band in the red part of the spectrum. The average time for the development of methaemoglobin was $3 \cdot 17 \pm 1 \cdot 15$ min for hydroxylamine, $5 \cdot 0 \pm 1 \cdot 79$ min for p-aminophenol and $45 \cdot 2 \pm 13 \cdot 9$ min for hydroquinone. The difference in the rates of methaemoglobin formation produced by hydroxylamine and p-aminophenol is not statistically significant ($t = 0 \cdot 86$; $P > 0 \cdot 5$); the difference between the rates of methaemoglobin formation with hydroxylamine and hydroquinone ($t = 3 \cdot 02$; $0 \cdot 02 > P > 0 \cdot 01$) and the difference for p-aminophenol and hydroquinone ($t = 2 \cdot 87$; $0 \cdot 02 > P > 0 \cdot 01$) are statistically significant. In general, therefore, the relative activities of reducing agents as chemoreceptor stimuli run parallel with their activities as methaemoglobin formers. This is consistent with the hypothesis that the activity of reducing agents as stimulators of the carotid body chemoreceptors depends on the rate at which they react in oxidation–reduction reactions.

The agents studied in the experiments just described belong to different classes of chemical compounds. Their only common feature is that they are all reducing agents. It is apparently this feature which explains their ability to cause excitation in the chemoreceptor apparatus of the carotid body.

It may be that adrenaline, which in high concentration causes excitation of the carotid chemoreceptors (Belen'kii, 1948a), also produces this effect by virtue of its reducing properties. The stimulating effect of acetaldehyde on chemoreceptors (Handovsky, 1934) is also best explained by its action as a reducing agent.

How do reducing agents act on the chemoreceptor apparatus in the carotid body?

Because of their power to give off electrons very rapidly, reducing agents can probably compete more or less successfully with the natural substrates of tissue respiration and thus retard their oxidation. Chemoreceptor excitation produced by reducing agents could thus be regarded as a form of hypoxic excitation. Cyanides and poisons with similar mechanisms of action cause chemoreceptor excitation by blocking the chain of oxidative reactions in its last link, that is by inactivating cytochrome oxidase, but reducing agents produce this effect by inhibiting oxidation processes in their initial or intermediate links. Naturally, different reducing agents, depending on the value of their oxidation–reduction potential, have their own particular effect on the various intermediate stages in the chain of oxidation reactions.

CHAPTER VI

Effect of Disturbances of Carbohydrate Metabolism in the Carotid Bodies on their Chemoreceptor Function

IT may be inferred from the experiments discussed in the preceding chapter that hypoxic excitation of carotid chemoreceptors is connected with metabolic changes in the chemoreceptor tissue. It can readily be imagined that the chemoreceptor excitation developing in hypoxaemia is, in the ultimate reckoning, a reaction not to lack of oxygen in the blood but to metabolic disturbances in the chemoreceptor cells themselves, dependent on this deficiency. This idea is not an original one. As we have already indicated (see Chapter IV), a number of investigators who support the "acid" theory of excitation of the chemoreceptor apparatus take this view. But while regarding the hypoxic excitatory process in chemoreceptors as the result of metabolic disturbances in the chemoreceptor cells, they do not associate the excitation of the chemoreceptor apparatus produced by other stimuli with disturbances of cell metabolism. Winder (1937), for example, concluded from his experiments that the excitatory effect of carbon dioxide on chemoreceptors, in contrast to the excitatory effect of hypoxia, is not connected with metabolic changes in the tissues of the carotid body.

Chernigovskii concluded from his experiments on the chemoreceptors in an isolated intestinal loop that there were fundamental differences in the mechanisms whereby different agents produced their excitatory effects on the chemoreceptor apparatus. He is of the opinion that carbon dioxide, oxygen lack and, probably, cyanide excite chemoreceptors by producing metabolic changes in the protoplasm of chemoreceptor cells; nicotine, acetylcholine, potassium chloride and similar substances act directly on the afferent nerve endings, "and for them the protoplasm is essentially only the route over which the particular chemical stimulus reaches the receptors" (Chernigovskii, 1943).

Belen'kii (1948a, 1951a) carried out some special experiments to determine the importance of metabolic changes in the tissue of the carotid body in relation to the development of excitation, in response to various forms of chemoreceptor stimulation.

In some experiments he studied the effect of experimentally produced disturbances of carbohydrate metabolism in the carotid body tissue on the excitability of its chemoreceptors in relation to various types of stimuli.

EXPERIMENTS WITH CARBOHYDRATE STARVATION OF THE CAROTID BODY

The effect of carbohydrate starvation of the carotid bodies on the excitability of the chemoreceptors was first tested.

In decerebrate cats the isolated carotid sinus was perfused with saline solution containing the concentrations of sodium, potassium and calcium usually present in Ringer–Locke fluid and also bicarbonate (the pH of the solution was 7·4–7·5) but no glucose. Rapid exhaustion of the carbohydrate reserves of the glomus cells was achieved by maintaining the temperature of the perfusion fluid at 42–43° and keeping it saturated with oxygen throughout the experiment. Under these conditions the effects of potassium cyanide, acetylcholine and, sometimes, those of nicotine also were tested every 15–20 min by injecting solutions into the perfusing fluid. The strength of the solutions injected was 1/10,000 for both cyanide and acetylcholine and 1/2500 for nicotine; the quantity injected was always 0·4 ml. Chemoreceptor excitation was assessed from the reflex respiratory reaction.

These experiments revealed that carbohydrate starvation of the carotid bodies led to gradual reduction of the reflex respiratory reactions to all the pharmacological agents tested. In some cases the reactions disappeared completely. But disappearance of the response to cyanide was never observed when that to acetylcholine remained present. When the perfusion fluid was changed to ordinary Ringer–Locke solution chemoreceptor excitability by all the stimuli tested was gradually restored. The reactions were generally, however, less intense than the original reactions.

These experiments thus showed that development of the

excitatory process in the chemoreceptors of the carotid body was connected with the metabolic state, irrespective of whether the stimulus was cyanide or acetylcholine.

EXPERIMENTS WITH ENZYME POISONS

In one series of experiments the normal course of carbohydrate metabolism in the carotid body tissues was disturbed by the local action of enzymatic poisons.

Disturbances of the processes of carbohydrate metabolism in the carotid body tissues were produced with mono-iodoacetate, fluoride, arsenite and malonate. These enzymatic poisons were perfused through the isolated carotid sinus. Chemoreceptor excitability was tested by injecting potassium cyanide (1/10,000–1/5000) and acetylcholine (1/5000–1/1000) solutions into the perfusing fluid. Excitability by lactic acid (0·05–0·5%) was also tested in a number of experiments. In all experiments 0·4 ml was injected into the perfusion fluid. As in the experiments just described, chemoreceptor excitation was assessed from the reflex respiratory response.

Mono-iodoacetate is regarded as an enzymatic poison, the main effect of which is retardation of glycolysis by inhibition of the enzymatic system for the oxidation of 3-phosphoglyceric aldehyde, but it may also have an inhibitory influence on other enzymatic systems.

Mono-iodoacetate solutions 1/10,000 (i.e. 1/500 M) and 1/5000 (i.e. 1/1000 M) were tested for their effect on the carotid body chemoreceptors. These solutions, which were prepared with Ringer–Locke fluid, were perfused through the isolated carotid sinus. This usually led to gradual increase in the rate and amplitude of the respiratory movements. There were then definite changes in the excitability of the chemoreceptors for their typical stimuli. Mono-iodoacetate reduced and abolished chemoreceptor excitability by cyanide and lactic acid more or less simultaneously. This result was at variance with Winder's observations (1937) that mono-iodoacetate abolished the reaction to hypoxia while reactions to acid stimuli (carbon dioxide) were still present. On the other hand, these results do agree with Chernigovskii's finding (1947b) that mono-iodoacetate abolished the excitability of chemoreceptors in an isolated intestinal loop for both hypoxic and acid stimuli.

The excitability of the chemoreceptors by acetylcholine was more resistant to mono-iodoacetate than their excitability by cyanide and lactic acid. It must, however, be emphasized that this difference was purely quantitative and not qualitative in character. When the tissues of the carotid body were exposed to mono-iodoacetate 1/1000 M there was disappearance of the reaction to acetylcholine as well as loss of excitability for cyanide and lactic acid (Fig. 17).

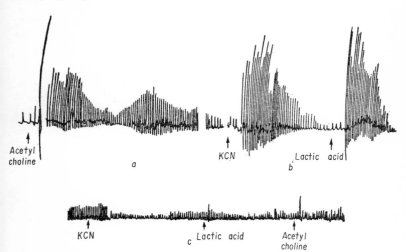

FIG. 17. Decerebrate cats. Perfusion of the isolated carotid sinus. Recording of respiration.
a, b—injection into the perfusing fluid of 0·4 ml of acetylcholine solution (1/10,000), potassium cyanide (1/5000) and lactic acid (0·5%). c—the same 17 min after the commencement of perfusion with mono-iodoacetate solution (1/5000).

The effect of mono-iodoacetate on chemoreceptor excitability was generally irreversible. This is consistent with the concept that mono-iodoacetate alkylates the thiol groups of enzymatic proteins.

The conclusion to be drawn from these experiments is, therefore, that the metabolic disturbances associated with mono-iodoacetate poisoning of the carotid body prevent the development of an excitatory process in the chemoreceptors to more or less the same degree in both hypoxia and exposure to acid. They also prevent the development of the excitatory process in response to acetylcholine, although to a lesser degree.

Fluoride Experiments

Verification of the results obtained with mono-iodoacetate was sought in experiments with fluoride, another substance which interferes with the glycolytic splitting of carbohydrates.

Fluoride solutions 1/10,000 (6/250 M) and 1/5000 (6/125 M) were used to poison the tissues of the carotid body. The perfusion of the isolated carotid sinus with fluoride produced more or less significant respiratory excitation in only occasional experiments.

When the carotid body was poisoned with fluoride there was a gradual and progressive decline of the reflex respiratory responses to cyanide, lactic acid and acetylcholine. A quite active reflex reaction to acetylcholine after complete disappearance of the reaction to cyanide was observed in only one of twenty experiments (Fig. 18).

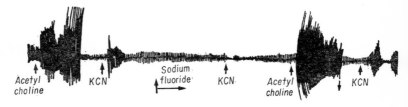

FIG. 18. Decerebrate cat. Perfusion of the isolated carotid sinus. Recording of respiration.
Injection into the perfusing fluid of 0·4 ml of each of the following solutions: acetylcholine (1/10,000); potassium cyanide (1/10,000). The horizontal arrow indicates the beginning of perfusion with a solution of sodium fluoride (1/10,000). The arrow pointing downwards indicates the commencement of flushing of the sinus with Ringer–Locke solution.

In some instances the reaction to acetylcholine persisted for some time after disappearance of the reaction to cyanide, but it was always very much attenuated in these cases. It would thus appear that the excitability of the chemoreceptors by acetylcholine is also modified by fluoride but somewhat more slowly and to a lesser extent than the excitability by cyanide and lactic acid.

This was confirmed when the sinus was washed free from fluoride. The fluoride effect, unlike that of mono-iodoacetate, was found to be reversible. Prolonged washing of the sinus with Ringer–Locke fluid usually led to restoration of chemoreceptor excitability. The reaction to acetylcholine was always restored before those to cyanide and lactic acid.

As sodium fluoride reacts with calcium chloride to form the insoluble calcium fluoride, it might be assumed that the fluoride effect depended on reduction in the calcium ion content of the Ringer–Locke fluid perfusing the isolated sinus. In control experiments to exclude this possibility, sodium fluoride was dissolved in Ringer–Locke fluid having an increased calcium chloride content. The calcium chloride content was calculated to ensure that the solution contained 0.02% $CaCl_2$ even after the maximum possible removal of calcium by fluoride. Ringer–Locke solution containing 0.33 g $CaCl_2/l$. was, therefore, used with $1/10,000$ M sodium fluoride; likewise, Ringer–Locke fluid with a $CaCl_2$ content of 0.46 g/l. was used with $1/5000$ M fluoride. Reduction and disappearance of the reflex reactions to cyanide, lactic acid and acetylcholine were observed in these experiments just as in the experiments described earlier.

The changes in chemoreceptor excitability associated with perfusion of the isolated sinus with fluoride solution developed after intervals which varied considerably (from 10 min to 1 hr) in different animals. It might be thought that, when perfusion was prolonged, a certain quantity of the fluoride might escape from the perfusion fluid into the circulation and reduce the excitability of the respiratory centre to reflex effects from the carotid sinus zone. This possibility was also excluded: in some of the experiments cyanide (0.05 mg/kg) was injected intravenously after reflex respiratory reactions from the isolated sinus in response to the test stimuli had disappeared. This invariably led to violent respiratory excitation—evidence of the excitability of the respiratory centre to reflexes which, under these conditions, reached it from the chemoreceptors in the carotid sinus region from the other side.

The results of the experiments with sodium fluoride were thus essentially in agreement with those with the mono-iodoacetate. Fluoride, like mono-iodoacetate, reduced or abolished chemoreceptor excitability for cyanide, lactic acid and acetylcholine.

There was a parallel reduction of the excitability by cyanide and lactic acid in all cases, a fact which contradicted the view that lactic acid is the immediate chemoreceptor stimulus in hypoxia. The excitability of the chemoreceptors by acetylcholine was reduced or even abolished by mono-iodoacetate and fluoride, and might merely occasionally persist somewhat longer than the excitability for cyanide and lactic acid.

Experiments with Arsenite and Malonate

Arsenite and malonate were used as enzymatic poisons with an action on the aerobic breakdown of carbohydrates.

According to Dickens (1941), the effect of arsenite develops slowly. In animal tissue homogenates As_2O_3 in dilution of $1/10,000$ M inhibits respiration by $50–100\%$ after 60 min; only in concentrations of the order of $1/1000$ M does As_2O_3 have an inhibitory effect on glycolysis.

The inhibiting effect of arsenite on respiration is connected with the fact that it blocks the sulphydryl groups of thiol enzymes (see Belen'kii and Rozengart, 1949). The effect of arsenite on the excitability of carotid body chemoreceptors was tested in experiments on the isolated carotid sinus of decerebrate cats. The sinus was perfused with $1/10,000$ ($1/500$ M), $1/25,000$ ($1/5000$ M) and $1/50,000$ ($1/10,000$ M) solutions of As_2O_3 in Ringer–Locke fluid.

Arsenite in all the concentrations tested produced marked reduction or even complete disappearance of reflex respiratory reactions to cyanide, lactic acid and acetylcholine. The order in which the excitabilities for the different stimuli disappeared varied in different experiments. Some degree of restoration of chemoreceptor excitability could be attained in most cases by prolonged washing of the sinus to free it from arsenite (Fig. 19); after some time, however, it again began to decline and ultimately disappeared.

Sodium malonate was tested for its effect on the excitability of the carotid body chemoreceptors in strengths of from 1 to $3\cdot7\%$ ($1/40–1/50$ M). When the stronger malonate solutions were perfused through the sinus there was a slight, gradually increasing, respiratory excitation. The same effect was observed when a small quantity of concentrated malonate solution was injected into Ringer–Locke fluid perfusing the sinus. The reflex respiratory excitation produced by malonate appeared to have a mechanism similar to that of cyanide: arrest of tissue respiration. The difference is that malonate, which inhibits the succinate–fumarate system, arrests oxidation processes at an earlier stage than cyanide, which blocks the final link in tissue respiration.

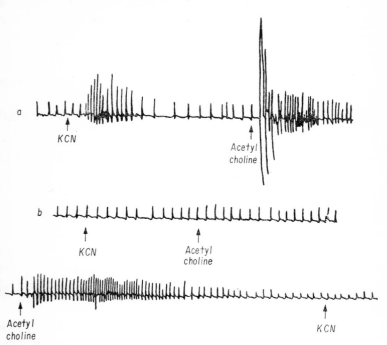

FIG. 19.   Decerebrate cat. Perfusion of the isolated carotid sinus.   Recording of respiration.
a—injection into the perfusing fluid of 0·4 ml of potassium cyanide solution (1/5000) and acetylcholine solution (1/5000). b—the same 25 min after the beginning of perfusion with arsenious anhydride (1/10,000). c—the same 40 min after the commencement of flushing of the sinus with Ringer–Locke solution.

When the carotid bodies were exposed to malonate the chemo-receptor sensitivity to cyanide was gradually reduced and finally abolished. The reaction to acetylcholine was also reduced but was more resistant to malonate than the reaction to cyanide. When the isolated sinus was washed out with Ringer–Locke solution, the reflex reactions to the test stimuli, which had been reduced or abolished, were quite rapidly restored (Fig. 20).

Examination of the effects of various agents interfering with the normal course of carbohydrate metabolism on the excitability of the carotid chemoreceptors all yielded generally similar results: all agents of this type reduced or abolished chemoreceptor excitability.

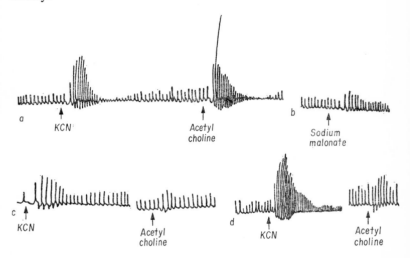

FIG. 20. Decerebrate cat. Perfusion of the isolated carotid sinus. Recording of respiration.
a—injection into the perfusing fluid of 0·4 ml of potassium cyanide solution (1/10,000) and acetylcholine (1/10,000). b—injection into the perfusing fluid of 0·6 ml of 0·75 M sodium malonate. c—the same as in a, 30 min after the beginning of perfusion with sodium malonate solution (0·067 M). d—the same 40 min after the commencement of flushing of the sinus with Ringer–Locke solution.

Chemoreceptor excitability for lactic acid always declined parallel with that for cyanide. This is at variance with the results of Winder's experiments (1937) and does not support the "acid" theory of carotid chemoreceptor function.

In a number of experiments the chemoreceptors could still be excited by acetylcholine when they had ceased to respond to cyanide or lactic acid. This difference was, however, only quantitative in character.

Two theories can be offered in explanation of the blocking effect of enzymatic poisons on the excitability of the carotid body chemoreceptors. The first is that enzymatic poisons prevent the stimulating agents from reacting with the corresponding systems in the chemoreceptor cells; the second possibility is that enzymatic poisons do not prevent "reception" of the chemical stimuli but create disturbances of metabolism in the glomus cells, which render development of the excitation process impossible.

The first theory must obviously be rejected completely inasmuch as all the enzymatic poisons used in the experiments were completely different from one another in chemical nature and yet blocked the chemoreceptor excitability for all the stimuli tested. There can be no doubt that cyanide, lactic acid and acetylcholine react with different biochemical structures in the protoplasm and it is extremely unlikely that all these structures would be blocked by each of the enzymatic poisons tested.

Of the enzymatic poisons used, only for fluoride are there published reports which would appear to indicate that it modifies chemoreceptor excitability through blocking of the "reception" of stimulating agents. There are reports on the blocking effect of fluoride on haemin enzymes (Lipman, 1929b) and, secondly, on its atropine-like effect (Mednikyan and Asratyan, 1951). The ability of fluoride to enter into reaction with components of the cytochrome system has not, however, been confirmed by later investigations (Borei, 1939), and the findings from which the atropine-like properties of fluoride were deduced admit of a different interpretation. The conclusion as to the atropine-like properties of fluoride was based by Mednikyan and Asratyan on experiments in which it was demonstrated that fluoride prevented the effects of acetylcholine in a number of biological test materials. More particularly, the blocking effect of fluoride on the excitability of the carotid chemoreceptors to acetylcholine was confirmed. Obviously, these results can be regarded not as the consequence of the blocking of cholinoreactive systems but as the result of disturbances of cell metabolism produced by fluoride, disturbances which make the excitatory process impossible (see Koshtoyants,

1945). The latter explanation is also supported by certain findings arrived at in Anichkov's laboratory. Studying the effect of sodium fluoride on the function of the superior cervical sympathetic ganglion, Grebenkina (1950, 1952) found that fluoride abolished the excitability of the ganglion cells both by acetylcholine and by stimulation of the preganglionic fibres. At the same time Vinikova (1950, 1952) established that fluoride had no material effect on the induced acetylcholine induced—or nicotine induced—secretion of adrenaline by the suprarenal glands. Fluoride thus prevented the acetylcholine effect in ganglion cells and in the chemoreceptor apparatus but not in the chromaffin cells of the suprarenal gland, although the cholinoreactive systems in all these structures are of the same type. The differences in the response of these structures to fluoride are obviously connected with differences in the nature of the metabolic processes that accompany excitation in ganglion and chemoreceptor cells, on the one hand, and in chromaffin cells of the suprarenal gland, on the other.

There is thus good reason to say that the blocking of chemoreceptor excitability in the carotid body as a result of the action of enzymatic poisons is due to a disturbance of cell metabolism which renders the development of the excitatory process impossible, and not on the effect of the poisons on the "reception" of the stimulating agents.

The process of excitation is characterized by certain definite changes in the biochemistry of the excited tissue ("metabolism of excitation"). These changes also constitute the basis of the electrical phenomena associated with the excitatory process (Chagovets, 1903; Koshtoyants, 1945; and others). Since chemoreceptor excitation may be produced by chemical agents of completely different nature, it must be accepted that the "metabolism of excitation" can be induced by action on different links in the chain of metabolic processes that occur in the chemoreceptor cells of the carotid bodies. The experimental results indicate that acetylcholine also induces chemoreceptor excitation by intervening in the biochemical dynamics of the receptor cells. The idea that acetylcholine is able to change the biochemical processes in the tissues is, of course, not original. It follows logically from the study of the trophic function of the nervous system. A number of experimental proofs of the involvement of acetylcholine in processes of tissue metabolism have been given by Koshtoyants and his co-workers (see Koshtoyants, 1945, 1947, 1948, 1950a, 1950b, 1951; Koshtoyants and Turpayev, 1946; Koshtoyants and Mogoras, 1946; Koshtoyants and Logunova, 1950).

Even if acetylcholine does not fulfil the function of mediator in the chemoreceptor apparatus of the carotid body, the possible genetic relationship between the glomus cells and the cells of autonomic ganglia would explain why acetylcholine is also capable of inducing "metabolism of excitation" in the glomus cells.

It would appear, therefore, that excitation of the carotid body chemoreceptors always depends on changes in metabolic processes within the chemoreceptor cells, irrespective of the agent that produces it. As "metabolism of excitation" can be induced by different chemical stimuli, acting on different reactive systems, the reactions produced by them may differ quantitatively in their resistance to the action of enzymatic poisons.

Belen'kii's experiments (1948c, 1951a), described in this chapter, show that the excitability of chemoreceptors is abolished both by enzymatic poisons acting mainly on glycolysis and by those mainly inhibiting tissue respiration. These results do not enable us to link chemoreceptor excitation with any particular reaction in carbohydrate metabolism. Completely normal carbohydrate metabolism must apparently be regarded as essential for the development of chemoreceptor excitation.

CHAPTER VII

Adenosine Triphosphate and the Chemoreceptor Function of the Carotid Bodies

THE experimental results described in the preceding chapter led to the conclusion that normal carbohydrate metabolism in the carotid bodies was essential for the functioning of their chemoreceptors. This conclusion is completely reconcilable with biochemical concept of carbohydrates as the main source of energy for the various functions of the animal organism. This has, however, been demonstrated mainly by study of the biochemical dynamics of muscle, and energy liberated by the breakdown of carbohydrates cannot be used directly for the performance of physiological work. In all respiration, just as in glycolysis, the energy liberated accumulates in the form of energy-rich bonds in certain organic phosphate compounds (see Engel'gardt, 1945, 1948; Soskin and Levin, 1946; Baldwin, 1949; Ivanov, 1950; Szent-Gyorgyi, 1960). These bonds are formed by the combination of inorganic phosphate with adenosine diphosphoric acid (ADP), the latter being converted to adenosine triphosphoric acid (ATP). This process of disappearance of inorganic phosphate occurs in certain intermediate processes in carbohydrate breakdown (Engel'gardt and Braunshtein, 1928; Engel'gardt, 1930; Belitser, 1939; and many others; see also Szent-Gyorgyi, 1960). Energy-rich phosphate bonds each contain 12,000 cal per mole phosphate. It is by the expenditure of this energy, liberated when the energy-rich phosphate bonds break down, that physiological work is performed (Lipman, 1941; Meyerhof, 1944).

In glycolysis three new energy-rich bonds are formed for each hexose radical glycolysed, which means that about 36,000 cal of energy is "captured". As the reduction in free energy for each hexose radical glycolysed is 57,000 cal, the quantity of energy "captured" in glycolysis by the formation of energy-rich bonds is upwards of 50% of the total energy liberated. Energywise, the aerobic breakdown of carbohydrates is more effective: it is thought that about forty-eight new energy-rich bonds are formed for each molecule of glucose oxidized, and this corresponds to the accumulation of at least 48,000 cal for each mole of glucose. As the reduction in free energy associated with the oxidation of a mole of glucose is approximately 68,000 cal, the quantity of energy "captured" in the course of the aerobic breakdown of carbohydrates is about 70% of the total liberated (see Baldwin, 1949).

These facts indicate that the formation of new energy-rich bonds is greatly reduced when there is change from aerobic to anaerobic conditions in the tissues. If the energy expenditure remains at its former level, the energy balance will inevitably become negative and this must lead to arrest of physiological functions as the energy reserves become exhausted.

There is now a very considerable body of experimental evidence that the most varied forms of vital activity are brought about by the expenditure of energy "trapped" in the form of the energy-rich bonds of ATP (see review by Boettge et al., 1957).

There was every reason to believe that the process of excitation in the carotid body chemoreceptors also rests on expenditure of energy from the energy-rich bonds of ATP. Belen'kii (1951b, 1952a, 1952b, 1953), therefore, undertook experiments to investigate the influence exerted by ATP on the function of the carotid body chemoreceptors. All his experiments were carried out on the isolated carotid sinuses of decerebrate cats. He tested the reaction of the chemoreceptors to cyanide, lactic acid and acetylcholine when the sinus was being perfused with Ringer–Locke fluid, without and with added sodium adenosine triphosphate solutions ($2 \cdot 7 \times 10^{-8}$ to $2 \cdot 7 \times 10^{-6}$ M).

The change-over from perfusion of the sinus with ordinary Ringer–Locke fluid to perfusion with ATP sometimes produced slight, gradually increasing, respiratory excitation of short duration. That ATP can cause excitation of the carotid body chemoreceptors was subsequently confirmed by Jarisch et al. (1952). This reaction was only seen in the experiments in which the ATP concentration in the perfusing fluid exceeded $2 \cdot 7 \times 10^{-7}$ M. The injection of stronger ATP solutions (of the order of 1/100,000) into the perfusing fluid never produced respiratory changes. It would appear that more or less prolonged action of ATP on the isolated carotid sinus is required if ATP is to produce respiratory excitation.

Whether or not ATP causes a respiratory response, it has the effect of greatly intensifying the reflex respiratory reaction to cyanide, acetylcholine or lactic acid (Fig. 21). The period during

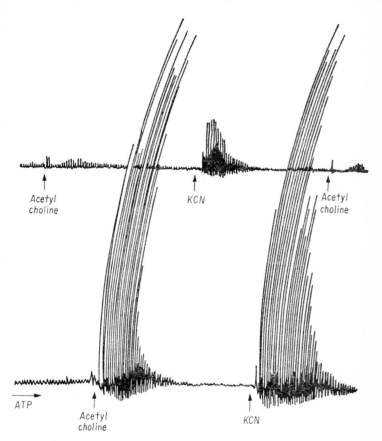

FIG. 21. Decerebrate cat. Isolated carotid sinus. Recording of respiration.
Above. Injection into the perfusing fluid of 0·4 ml of acetyl-choline solution (1/10,000) and potassium cyanide (1/5000).
Below. The same 1 min and 3 min after the commencement of perfusion with ATP solution (2·7 × 10⁻⁷ M).

which the reflex reactions were intensified was of short duration (less than 5 min) in some experiments but in others it lasted up to 40 min. Later, the ATP perfusion being continued, the intensity of the respiratory reactions to the test stimuli diminished gradually to below the initial levels; sometimes the reactions disappeared completely or almost completely. In a few experiments no period of intensified reflex reactions could be detected at any time during perfusion; the reactions declined right from the start of the perfusion of the sinus with ATP.

Markedly enhanced reflex respiratory responses to cyanide, lactic acid and acetylcholine were always observed after perfusion with the ATP, during the period when the sinus was being washed through with Ringer–Locke fluid. This second period of intensified reflex responses was generally quite prolonged (up to 3 hr or more) (Figs. 22 and 23). In some experiments the sinus was again perfused with ATP solution during this period. This generally led, after a certain time, to fresh reduction in the intensity of the respiratory reactions. When the sinus was again flushed with Ringer–Locke solution there was fresh intensification of the reactions in some instances.

An interesting point is that in the experiments in which no respiratory reactions to the test stimuli were observed before the ATP perfusion and in which it might be thought that the integrity of the reflex arc had been destroyed during the isolation of the sinus, test stimuli not infrequently began to produce active reflex reactions during and particularly after the period of ATP perfusion (during lavage of the sinus). This suggested that the absence of reflex reactions from the chemoreceptors when the experiments were carried out on the isolated carotid sinus might be connected with some particular change in the functional state of the chemoreceptors produced by ATP and not with faulty surgical technique.

Control experiments were carried out to prove that the observed effect was the result of the action of ATP on the chemoreceptor apparatus of the carotid body and not a consequence of leakage into the general circulation through vessels left untied and a direct action on the respiratory centre. These experiments were carried out in two forms: in some cyanide and acetylcholine were injected as usual into the perfusing fluid and ATP (2 ml of 2.7×10^{-3} M solution) was injected into a femoral vein; in others both ATP

N

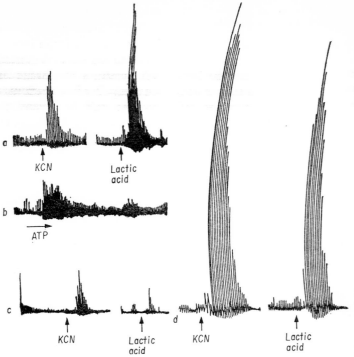

FIG. 22. Decerebrate cat. Isolated carotid sinus. Recording
of respiration.
a—injection into the perfusing fluid of 0·4 ml of potassium
cyanide solution (1/625,000) and lactic acid solution (1/1600).
b—beginning of perfusion of the sinus with ATP solution
(5 × 10⁻⁷ M). c—injection into the perfusing fluid of cyanide
and lactic acid solutions 20 and 25 min after the commencement
of perfusion with ATP solution. d—the same 10 and 15 min after
the commencement of flushing of the sinus with Ringer–Locke
solution.

and the chemoreceptor stimuli were injected intravenously. The
intensities of the respiratory reactions to the test stimuli were unchanged by ATP in these control experiments.

It was thus obvious that the intensification of the reflexes from
the carotid body chemoreceptors produced by ATP was due to
the effect of this substance on the peripheral chemoreceptor
apparatus.

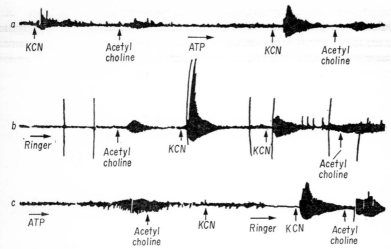

FIG. 23. Decerebrate cat. Isolated carotid sinus. Recording of respiration.

a—injection into the perfusing fluid of 0·4 ml of potassium cyanide solution (1/20,000) and acetylcholine (1/20,000) during perfusion of the sinus with Ringer–Locke fluid and also during perfusion with ATP solution (2·7 × 10⁻⁵). b—the same when the sinus was being flushed with Ringer–Locke solution. c—the same during repeated perfusion with ATP solution and flushing with Ringer–Locke fluid.

These experimental results have since been confirmed by other investigators (Raskova *et al.*, 1955, 1956; see also the review of Boettge *et al.*, 1957).

ATP apparently intensifies reflex reactions from other chemoreceptor zones as well as from the chemoreceptors in the carotid body. At any rate, Belen'kii and Tomilina (1951) observed definite intensification of the pressor reaction in response to acetylcholine from the chemoreceptors in a loop of cat intestine, isolated by Chernigovskii's method, after perfusion of the vessels in the intestinal loop with ATP solution (7 × 10⁻⁷ M).

The ATP-induced intensification of reflex reactions to stimulation of the carotid chemoreceptors can be explained by the fact that ATP functions as the donor of energy for the excitatory process. Reduction of the excitability of the chemoreceptor apparatus by enzymatic poisons inhibiting the breakdown of carbohydrates is quite consistent with this explanation; in actual fact the inhibition of carbohydrate metabolism must of necessity be associated with reduced formation of energy-rich bonds and, in consequence, with reduction of the energy resources of the tissues.

The importance of ATP as a source of energy for the functioning of the carotid bodies will also explain the inhibition of the chemo-receptor reflexes resulting from prolonged stimulation of the chemoreceptor apparatus.

Studying the effects of cyanides on the carotid body chemo-receptors, Mel'nikova (1947, 1952) found that, when the isolated sinus was perfused with cyanide solution, the respiratory excita-tion, at first quite acute, faded somewhat rapidly and was replaced by respiratory depression. In other words, when exposed to cyanide for long periods, the chemoreceptors reacted at first by excitation but later became inexcitable. Mel'nikova showed that the rate at which the chemoreceptors lost their excitability increased with increasing cyanide concentration. When the sinus was washed with Ringer–Locke fluid, the excitability of the chemoreceptors was gradually restored, and the weaker the solution of cyanide that had been used, the more rapid was this process.

Anichkov and Belen'kii (1948) found that prolonged perfusion of the isolated sinus with cyanide solution ultimately abolished reflex respiratory reactions to acetylcholine as well as reactions to cyanide. Analysis showed that this effect depended on the functional state of the peripheral chemoreceptor apparatus and not on reduced excitability of the respiratory centre, as the intravenous injection of cyanide under these conditions produced pronounced respira-tory excitation just as before, this excitation being then dependent on a reflex from the chemoreceptors in the contralateral carotid body.

It might be suggested that "cyanide inhibition" of the chemo-receptors could be explained by exhaustion of the energy reserves in the chemoreceptor tissue as a result of the prolonged action of cyanide, which arrests tissue respiration and, consequently, the regeneration of energy-rich compounds at the same time as exciting the chemoreceptors.

In experiments to test this theory (Belen'kii, 1951b, 1952a,

1952b) the isolated carotid sinus in decerebrate cats was perfused with potassium cyanide solution (3×10^{-4} M) until clearly evident respiratory depression developed. This usually occurred after 3–4 min. The perfusion of the sinus with cyanide solution being continued, 3–4 ml of ATP solution 3.4×10^{-5} M was then injected by means of a syringe into the stream of perfusion fluid. This always led to pronounced respiratory excitation; the "cyanide inhibition" could thus be abolished by ATP (Fig. 24), an effect

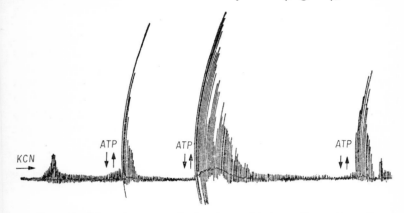

Fig. 24. Decerebrate cat. Isolated carotid sinus. Recording of respiration. Perfusion of the sinus with potassium cyanide solution (1/50,000). The arrows pointing downwards and upwards indicate the beginning and end of the injection into the perfusing fluid of ATP solution (3.4×10^{-5} M).

which could be reproduced repeatedly. These experiments, in which "cyanide inhibition" was abolished by ATP, affords weighty confirmation of the concept of ATP as the donor of energy for development of the excitatory process in the chemoreceptors of the carotid body.

Observations made in the laboratory in which the authors of this book worked together revealed that the chemoreceptors were also depressed by prolonged perfusion of the isolated sinus with acetylcholine. This depression was always regarded as a manifestation of block of the cholinoreactive systems by excess of acetylcholine ("persistent depolarization"), but the experiments with "cyanide inhibition" of chemoreceptors suggest that the effect of ATP should always be tested in relation to "acetylcholine inhibition" (Belen'kii, 1951b).

The isolated carotid sinus of the cat was perfused with acetylcholine 1/100,000–1/50,000. The same phenomena as in perfusion with cyanide solutions were observed: there was very active respiratory excitation, rapidly replaced by respiratory inhibition, and within 2 or 3 min the amplitude of the respiratory movements had reached or might even fall below its initial value. The injection of 3 ml $3{\cdot}4 \times 10^{-5}$ M ATP solution into the perfusion fluid during the continuous perfusion of the sinus with acetylcholine led after a short time to a fresh wave of excitation (Fig. 25). This phenomenon could be reproduced repeatedly just as in the experiments with "cyanide inhibition". These experiments obviously confirm the importance of ATP as source energy for the functioning of the carotid chemoreceptors.

Raskova *et al.* (1956) have shown that chemoreceptor sensitivity

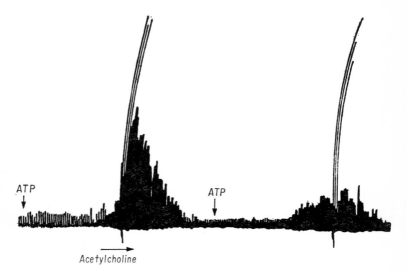

FIG. 25. Decerebrate cat. Isolated carotid sinus. Recording of respiration.

The arrows pointing downwards indicate injection into the perfusing fluid of 3 ml ATP solution ($3{\cdot}4 \times 10^{-5}$ M). The horizontal arrow shows the beginning of perfusion of the sinus with acetylcholine solution (1/100,000).

to acetylcholine and potassium chloride, abolished by the action of bacterial toxins, could also be restored by ATP and AMP.

It is possible that the process which has been termed receptor adaptation may sometimes also be due to impoverishment of the receptor tissue in compounds with energy-rich bonds.

Belen'kii (1951b, 1952a) tested the effect of adenosine monophosphate (AMP) solutions on the function of the carotid chemoreceptors. The isolated carotid sinus in cats was perfused with AMP solutions $2 \cdot 7 \times 10^{-7}$ to $2 \cdot 7 \times 10^{-10}$ M.

This had no significant effect on the animals' respiration. But AMP in concentrations of $2 \cdot 7 \times 10^{-7}$ and $2 \cdot 7 \times 10^{-9}$ M intensified the reactions to cyanide, lactic acid and acetylcholine. This intensification was seen mainly after the action of AMP, during perfusion of the sinus with Ringer–Locke solution (Fig. 26).

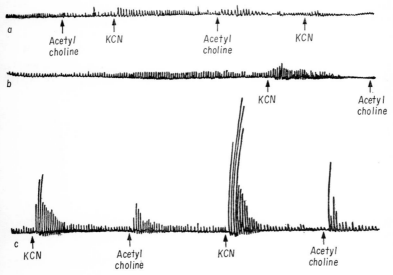

Fig. 26. Decerebrate cat. Isolated carotid sinus. Recording of respiration.
a—perfusion with Ringer–Locke fluid. Injection into the perfusing fluid of 0·4 ml potassium cyanide solution (1/10,000) and acetylcholine solution. b—the same during perfusion of the sinus with adenosine monophosphate solution ($2 \cdot 7 \times 10^{-7}$ M). c—the same 8 min after the commencement of flushing of the sinus with Ringer–Locke fluid.

Investigating chemoreceptors in various tissues (rabbit ear, rabbit intestine and kidney, cat intestine and kidney), Gava and Raskova (1960) have recently found that, like ATP, AMP increases the sensitivity of chemoreceptors to acetylcholine and restores their reactivity when they have been blocked by the toxin of *Shigella shigae* or by typhoid endotoxin; these effects were not observed with adenine. On the evidence of their experiments, Gava and Raskova questioned the importance of the energy-rich bonds of ATP for the functioning of chemoreceptors and suggested that the low-energy bond of adenine with phosphoric acid was of greater importance for chemoreceptor function.

It is of interest to note that, in experiments on the rectus abdominis muscle of the frog, Babskii *et al.* (1945) likewise observed that AMP, as well as ATP, intensified contractile reactions to acetylcholine. This was explained by the possible conversion of AMP to ATP in the muscle. This idea can be extended with even greater probability to chemoreceptor tissues, as respiration in these tissues is many times more intense than in muscle tissue (Daly *et al.*, 1954). It should be added that tissue respiration is rendered even more intense in the presence of AMP (Belitser, 1939).

CHAPTER VIII

New Concepts on the Mechanism Responsible for Development of the Excitatory Process in the Chemoreceptors of the Carotid Body

WE know that the role of ATP in muscle tissue is not merely that of a source of energy for contractile activity. ATP has been proved to be directly concerned in the actual mechanics of muscular contraction in that it interacts with the carrier of adenosine triphosphatase activity, the contractile protein myosin, thus altering the mechanical properties of the latter (Lyubimova and Engel'gardt, 1939; Engel'gardt, 1941; Engel'gardt and Lyubimova, 1942; Engel'gardt, 1945, 1948).

This raises the question of whether the development of excitation in the carotid body may not be connected with the metabolism of energy-rich phosphate bonds in the chemoreceptor cells. Consideration of certain published biochemical and pharmacological findings suggest that this is so.

Substances are known which have inhibitory effects on the regeneration of energy-rich bonds without reducing the intensity of tissue respiration, or, in other words, which lead to a dissociation of oxygen consumption by, and the accumulation of energy stores in, the tissues. These poisons destroy the biological meaning of tissue respiration; it becomes "useless", "futile" (Engel'gardt).

The effects of poisons that dissociate oxidative phosphorylation from respiration have been studied in detail by Seits and Engel'gardt (1949a, 1949b) in experiments on nucleated red cells, on baker's yeast and on tumour cells. Four poisons were examined: 2,4-dinitrophenol, sodium azide, sodium nitrite and methylene blue. In concentrations which did not reduce and might sometimes even increase (2,4-dinitrophenol) the consumption of oxygen, all these substances produced inhibition of the disappearance of inorganic phosphate and a reduction in the quantity of readily hydrolysed

ATP phosophate. In other words, these substances inhibited respiratory phosphorylation. Yet another feature was demonstrated in the action of these poisons: they all led under aerobic conditions to the formation of lactic acid, which meant that they inhibited the "Pasteur effect". The authors referred to were of the opinion that the simultaneous appearance of "dissociating" and "anti-Pasteur" effects was not due to chance but depended "on the existence of a definite connexion between the two now known functions of cell respiration, namely the Pasteur effect and the generation of energy-rich phosphatic bonds".

The inhibitory effect of 2,4-dinitrophenol on oxidative phosphorylation has also been demonstrated by Loomis and Lipman (1948).

A point of extreme interest is that there are references to the stimulating effects on carotid body chemoreceptors in respect of three of the four poisons studied by Seits and Engel'gardt. This was demonstrated for 2,4-dinitrophenol by Shen and Hauss (1939) in experiments on dogs. These investigators showed that the injection of 0·4 mg 2,4-dinitrophenol into the carotid artery led to dyspnoea; this did not occur if the poison was injected after denervation of the carotid sinus region. The stimulating effect of 2,4-dinitrophenol on chemoreceptors was confirmed again later by Jarisch et al. (1952). The excitatory effect of sodium azide on the carotid body chemoreceptors was demonstrated by Anichkov (1945). This effect of azide might, of course, be explained by the fact that, like the cyanides, it inhibits cytochrome oxidase activity and thus tissue respiration (Keilin, 1936). However, according to Seits and Engel'gardt, azide interferes with oxidative phosphorylation but has practically no inhibitory effect on respiration in a concentration of $3·3 \times 10^{-3}$ M, which corresponds approximately to a dilution of 1:5000. In Anichkov's experiments respiratory excitation was observed even when 0·5 ml of a 1:20,000 sodium azide solution was injected into the dog's carotid artery. As this solution was, of course, diluted by the blood, its concentration would be even lower before it reached the carotid body. There is, therefore, reason to believe that the excitatory effect of sodium azide on the chemoreceptors observed in Anichkov's experiments was produced by concentrations of the substance which did not inhibit respiration but exhibited a "dissociating" effect.

Heymans *et al.* (1931e) had already demonstrated the stimulating effect on the carotid body chemoreceptors of sodium nitrite, the "dissociating" properties of which on oxidation and phosphorylation were first described by Shapot (1945). Heymans *et al.* observed the development of dyspnoea when 0·5 mg sodium nitrite was injected into the carotid artery of the dog. When sodium nitrite was injected into a carotid artery, the sinus region of which had been denervated, no respiratory excitation was noted. Only the remaining "dissociating" poison of the four studied by Seits and Engel'gardt, methylene blue, the "dissociating" properties of which were first demonstrated by Engel'gardt and Shapot (1935), had not previously been examined for its effect on the chemoreceptor apparatus of the carotid body.

Belen'kii investigated this aspect of the pharmacological activity of methylene blue (1949b, 1952a, 1952b).

A 1% solution of methylene blue was injected intravenously in doses of 6·9 to 10·0 mg/kg in decerebrate cats. This led to pronounced but transient respiratory excitation and increase of blood pressure. When the carotid sinus region had been excluded by infiltration of the surrounding tissues with procaine (1 ml of a 1% solution), injection of the same dose of methylene blue either no longer produced respiratory excitation or the excitation was extremely feeble. In the same way the blood pressure response was abolished, reduced or even reversed. These experiments thus showed that reflexes arising from the carotid sinus region were concerned in the action of methylene blue on respiration and circulation.

The influence of methylene blue on the carotid chemoreceptors was confirmed in experiments on the isolated carotid sinus in decerebrate cats. Methylene blue was tested in these experiments in dilutions of 1:20,000–1:5000. Reflex respiratory excitation was sometimes produced by dilutions of 1:20,000, but more constantly with 1:10,000 (Fig. 27).

Comparison of published findings for 2,4-dinitrophenol and sodium nitrite with our own findings for sodium azide and methylene blue led us to the general conclusion that a stimulating effect on the chemoreceptors of the carotid body was a property common to poisons rendering tissue respiration "futile".

The ability of such poisons to cause excitation in chemoreceptors is not apparently limited to those in the carotid bodies. Belen'kii and Tomilina (1951) studied the effect of 2,4-dinitrophenol, sodium nitrite and methylene blue on the chemoreceptors in loops of ileum isolated by Chernigovskii's method in decerebrate cats. The injection of 0·5% 2,4-dinitrophenol, 5–10% sodium nitrite or 0·1–1·0% methylene blue (always in quantities of 1 ml) into the Ringer–Locke solution perfusing the vessels of the intestinal loop produced a reflex increase of blood pressure sometimes associated with more or less pronounced respiratory excitation.

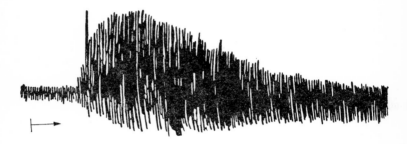

Fig. 27. Decerebrate cat. Isolated carotid sinus. Recording of respiration. Perfusion of the sinus with methylene blue solution (1/10,000).

It is thus highly probable that the power to react by excitation to poisons rendering tissue respiration "useless" is a general feature of the tissues of chemoreceptors.

Since poisons which render tissue respiration "useless" cause resynthesis of energy-rich bonds to lag behind their breakdown, they have the effect of rendering the energy balance in chemo-receptor tissue negative. It may, therefore, be considered that the chemoreceptor excitation resulting from the action of such agents, which are of very varied chemical nature, is the reaction to a negative shift in the energy balance.

There is no doubt that hypoxia, the adequate physiological stimulus of the chemoreceptors in the carotid body, produces a negative shift in the energy balance (Laves, 1956). The energy balance must be changed in exactly the same way by the action of cyanide, which represents a pharmacological form of tissue hypoxia.

It is, therefore, obvious that the intimate mechanism for the hypoxic excitation of chemoreceptors must be similar to the mechanism for the excitation produced by poisons which render respiration valueless.

The chemoreceptor excitation produced by acidosis can also be regarded as the result of a negative shift in the energy balance. The accumulation of acid products in the tissues is known to suppress tissue respiration and at the same time the production of energy-rich phosphate bonds (see, for example, Belitser and Tsybakova, 1939).

Whether this mechanism can be extended to the action of acetylcholine and cholinomimetic substances requires special investigation, and it would be premature to discuss it here.

The concept of a negative energy balance as the immediate cause of excitation in the chemoreceptors of the carotid body thus affords a completely satisfactory explanation of the mechanism of action of most typical stimuli on chemoreceptors.

Heymans and Neil (1958) are of the opinion that this view of the mechanism responsible for the functioning of chemoreceptor apparatus offers greater promise.

The concept that chemoreceptor excitation develops when the ATP content of the chemoreceptor tissue declines is also supported by Belen'kii's experiments, described in the previous chapter. It was noted in these experiments that prolonged perfusion of the isolated carotid sinus with ATP reduced the reflex responses to cyanide, acetylcholine and lactic acid. The ATP thus introduced from the outside apparently compensated to some degree for the decline in the content of ATP in the chemoreceptor tissue which resulted from the application of the stimuli to the chemoreceptor apparatus.

The mechanisms whereby a breakdown of ATP, not made good by resynthesis, leads to excitation in the chemoreceptor apparatus is still, of course, obscure.

If the reason for the development of excitation in the chemoreceptors of the carotid bodies lies in predominance of ATP breakdown over resynthesis, the intensity of the excitation which develops should be directly proportional to the energy potential of the chemoreceptor cells at the moment of the development of excitation, or in other words, directly proportional to the store of

ATP present in these cells. Great intensification of the reflex responses to all chemoreceptor stimuli can be produced by artificial enrichment of the carotid body in adenosine triphosphate.

Conversely, exhaustion of the energy stores in chemoreceptor cells by prolonged exposure to cyanide or acetylcholine renders these cells incapable of excitation, but their excitability is restored by applying ATP to the carotid body.

The loss of chemoreceptor excitability that results from the action of enzymatic poisons inhibiting carbohydrate metabolism can also be explained by exhaustion of ATP stores. Since the synthesis of energy-rich phosphate bonds is associated with the breakdown of carbohydrates, inhibition of the breakdown at any stage must lead to more or less pronounced impoverishment of the tissues in compounds with energy-rich bonds (Belitser and Tsybakova, 1939).

These views on the mechanism responsible for chemoreceptor function in the carotid body suggest that the signals reaching the central nervous system from these chemoreceptors ultimately convey information to the nerve centres on the unfavourable state of the energy balance in the tissues at the periphery. The tonic nature of the carotid body chemoreceptor function indicates that the energy balance in the chemoreceptor cells is extremely unstable. It is only because of this that chemoreceptor cells can fulfil the function of serving as an apparatus that responds rapidly to all unfavourable changes in the energy balance.

It will be realized that the carotid bodies perform a very delicate function in the body; they notify the central nervous system, not of serious energy disturbances when these have actually developed, but of the fairly remote threat of such disturbances, when the body's stores of energy-rich bonds begin to be expended.

If it is accepted that the physiological role of the carotid chemoreceptors is to signal the threat of energy deficiency, the reflexes associated with this activity should be regarded as being directed primarily to the removal of this threat.

CHAPTER IX

Reflexes Developing During Excitation of the Carotid Chemoreceptors; Their Paths and Physiological Significance

REFLEX respiratory excitation constitutes the most striking reaction to excitation of the carotid chemoreceptors. It has been described to follow the injection of all pharmacological agents with selective stimulating effects on the carotid chemoreceptors without exception. The degree of respiratory excitation produced by reflexes from carotid chemoreceptors can be assessed from the volume of ventilation during the action of reflex respiratory analeptics, such as lobeline, cytisine and Corconium which, as was explained earlier (Chapter II), produce respiratory excitation through a reflex from the carotid chemoreceptors.

Zakusov (1933, 1934) measured the respiratory volume in decerebrate cats after the intravenous injection of lobeline. The respiratory volume increased to twice its original value or more during the first minute after the injection of lobeline. Mikhel'son et al. (1957) made some accurate measurements of the respiratory volume in healthy subjects during carotid chemoreceptor excitation by testing the effect of Corconium. In man, the subcutaneous injection of Corconium, which has a selective stimulating effect on carotid chemoreceptors, increased the minute volume of respiration, which reached 20–40 l. during the period of maximum effect. The respiratory excitation produced by reflexes from the carotid chemoreceptors when stimulated with various pharmacological agents (acetylcholine, lobeline, cytisine, cyanide, sulphide) was reflected in the electrical activity of the main and ancillary respiratory muscles (Fedorchuk, 1956, 1957). There was a sharp increase in the electrical activity of the diaphragm, mainly as a result of increase in the amplitude of the oscillations and prolongation of the bursts of impulses during the

193

inspiratory period (Fig. 28). The electrical activity of the inter-
costal muscles showed similar changes. The ancillary respiratory
muscles developed electrical activity synchronous with respiration,
but in the abdominal muscles, unlike in the others, it was synchronous with the period of expiration. It is noteworthy that the
respiratory reflexes from the carotid bodies, transmitted over the
phrenic nerves, were mainly ipsilateral in Fedorchuk's experiments. When the carotid body on one side was removed, the

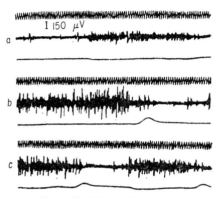

FIG. 28. Decerebrate cat.
From above down: time (0·02 sec); action potentials of diaphragm; respiration. a—during quiet respiration. b, c—after
injection of acetylcholine 0·2 ml into the fluid perfusing the
isolated carotid sinus.

intravenous injection of pharmacological agents producing
excitation of the carotid bodies (sodium sulphide 1 mg/kg or
cytisine 0·02 mg/kg) led to an increase of electrical impulses mainly
in the phrenic nerve on the side on which the the carotid body
was still present, that is the side from which the reflexes stimulating respiration came (Fig. 29). Carotid body excitation was also
reflected to some extent in the electrical activity of the limb
muscles.

In experiments on decerebrate cats with rigidity and corresponding electrical activity in the muscles, depression of the
electrical activity in the muscles was observed immediately after
excitation of the carotid chemoreceptors, but after 6 sec this was
replaced by increased activity (Fig. 30), the increase coinciding

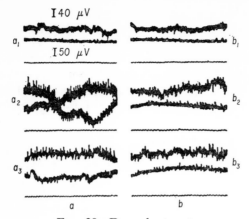

Fig. 29. Decerebrate cat.
From above down: oscillograms of the right and left phrenic nerves; time (0·02 sec). a—with the carotid sinus zones intact. b—with the carotid sinus (left) denervated. a_1 and b_1—during quiet respiration. a_2 and a_3, b_2 and b_3—after the intravenous injection of 0·3 ml 0·1% cytisine solution.

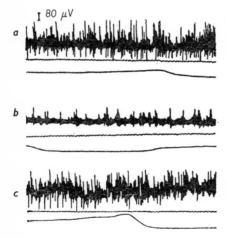

Fig. 30.   Decerebrate cat.   Decerebrate rigidity.
From above down: oscillogram of the quadriceps muscle; time (0·02 sec); mechanogram of respiration. a—a background of rigidity before stimulation of the carotid sinus zone. b—immediately after the injection of sodium sulphide into the fluid perfusing the isolated sinus. c—the same 6 sec later.

with the development of dyspnoea. When there was no rigidity, only this phase of electrical excitation in the limb muscles, coincident with the development of dyspnoea, was observed.

Fedorchuk concluded from her experiments that the phase of electrical depression in the skeletal muscles was the result of a direct reflex from the carotid chemoreceptors and the phase of excitation, an indirect effect produced through the respiratory centre.

Powerful excitation of the respiratory centre through reflexes from the carotid bodies is the most characteristic and constant reaction associated with the action of chemical substances on these structures. Inhibition of respiration was, however, seen under some conditions. Very transient respiratory arrest was sometimes seen at the very commencement of the action of powerful carotid chemoreceptor stimulants on the isolated carotid sinus.

When substances that stimulated the carotid chemoreceptors were allowed to act on the isolated carotid sinus for long periods, the respiratory excitation was followed by decline in respiratory amplitude and rate.

An important point is that the increase in the volume of respiration produced by reflexes from the carotid chemoreceptors is largely due to deepening of respiration, which undoubtedly has its own special physiological significance.

We know that the extent to which the alveolar air is oxygenated, or more accurately, the partial pressure of oxygen in the alveolar air, depends on the depth of respiration. Consequently, a reflex from the carotid bodies to the respiratory centre leads to increase in the partial pressure of oxygen in the alveolar air. The increased pulmonary ventilation and the associated increase in the partial pressure of oxygen in the alveolar air also promote the reflex dilatation of the bronchi which develops when the carotid chemoreceptors are stimulated (Daly and Schweitzer, 1951).

The degree of oxygen saturation of the blood, which is the main factor determining the oxygen supply to the tissues, is directly dependent on the partial pressure of oxygen in the alveolar air.

The reflexes originating from carotid body excitation are thus reactions which ensure the supply of oxygen to the tissues.

The physiological significance of these carotid body reactions to hypoxia was recognized when it was discovered that the carotid bodies were sensitive to oxygen lack.

The oxygen content of the blood is determined, however, by the oxygen capacity of the blood as well as by its oxygen tension. Oxygen capacity depends on the quantity of haemoglobin and the number of red cells in the circulating blood.

Investigations carried out in our laboratory have shown that, when the carotid chemoreceptors are excited, there is reflex contraction of the spleen with expulsion of red cells into the circulating blood (Belen'kii and Stroikov, 1950). The reflex contraction of the spleen caused by excitation of the carotid chemoreceptors is prevented by Sympatholytin; thus, the sympathetic innervation of the spleen or adrenomedullary secretion, or both mechanisms together, are concerned in the transmission of the reflex.

Experiments on cats revealed that the number of red cells in the circulating blood could increase by 20 per cent or more during excitation of the carotid chemoreceptors. There was a corresponding increase in the oxygen capacity of the blood, and this together with a simultaneous increase in the oxygen saturation of the blood would increase the oxygen supply to the tissues considerably.

It is difficult to doubt the physiological importance of this combined effect of reflexes from the carotid chemoreceptors on the oxygen saturation and oxygen capacity of the blood.

Numerous investigations have shown that excitation of the carotid chemoreceptors by various substances leads to reflex increase of blood pressure.

Experiments carried out by Fedorchuk (1954) with small doses of nicotine showed that the increase of blood pressure associated with excitation of the carotid chemoreceptors was due mainly to increase of adrenomedullary secretion, the direct vascular reflex being of lesser importance in this reaction. It is important to note that redistribution of blood was observed along with an increase of blood pressure produced by reflexes from the carotid chemoreceptors. The volumes of blood circulating in the extremities and intestinal vessels were reduced (Bernthal, 1932, 1934, 1938; Heymans *et al.*, 1935; Bernthal and Schwind, 1945) and the volume of the renal circulation remained unchanged

(Zakusov, 1938). As the general blood pressure was increased, the blood supply to brain and heart were obviously increased.

If we regard the reflexes from the carotid body as merely having the physiological significance of a means to restore the oxygen supply of the tissues when this is disturbed, the cycle of physiologically important reflexes would be limited to those which we have already examined.

In the concept we have developed, the carotid chemoreceptor reflexes are directed to maintain the level of the energy stores in the tissues and to restore these stores when they are depleted. From this standpoint carotid chemoreceptor excitation should lead to mobilization of the factors essential for the accumulation and restoration of energy stores in the tissues, including phosphate and other energy-rich bonds, as well as increasing the oxygen supply to the tissues (Fig. 31).

We know that the main source of energy in the body is the aerobic process of tissue respiration and that its substrate is glucose.

Investigations carried out in our laboratory have shown that reflex hyperglycaemia develops in response to excitation of the carotid chemoreceptors (Petropavlovskaya, 1953). This hyperglycaemia is clearly evident in decerebrate cats within 15 min of applying stimulus to the carotid chemoreceptors and reaches its maximum in 30 min, after which time the sugar content gradually declines and reaches its original level 1·5 hr after the beginning of stimulation.

Hyperglycaemia is not produced by excitation of the carotid chemoreceptors in adrenalectomized animals. The main factor in the development of hyperglycaemia is apparently reflex adreno-medullary secretion of the hormones which mobilize sugar from liver glycogen.

Working in our laboratory, Tomilina* has recently shown that carotid chemoreceptor excitation is associated with increase of the insulin activity of the blood and that this apparently depends on a reflex acting upon the pancreas as well as on hyper-adrenalinaemia.

Increase of adrenaline and noradrenaline secretion as a reflex

* ANICHKOV and TOMILINA. *Archives Internationales de Pharmaco-dynamie.* Heymans' 70th Anniversary Volume (1962).

from the carotid chemoreceptors has been demonstrated in our laboratory by various tests and with various chemoreceptor stimuli (Fedorchuk, 1954; Poskalenko, 1955; Anichkov *et al.*, 1960). There was increased secretion of both adrenaline and

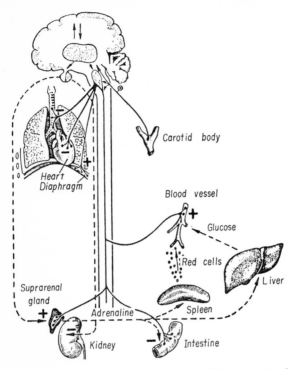

FIG. 31. Diagram of the reflex reactions arising on stimulation of the carotid chemoreceptors.

noradrenaline. The increase in the secretion of adrenaline induced by reflexes from the chemoreceptors was greater than the increase in the reaction from the baroreceptors produced by a fall of pressure in the carotid artery, in which case the adrenal secretion is predominantly one of noradrenaline (see Chapter I). The qualitative differences between the secretion of the adrenal medulla in relation to chemical stimulation of the carotid receptors and the secretion associated with change of pressure in the sinuses must be considered when the physiological role of chemo-receptor reflexes is being evaluated. Noradrenaline is known to possess a mainly pressor effect whereas adrenaline acts more powerfully on carbohydrate metabolism. The predominant secretion of adrenaline in the reflex to the adrenal medulla from the carotid chemoreceptors indicate that the main importance of these reflexes lies in the maintenance and restoration of the energy balance in the tissue, one means to which is increase of carbo-hydrate metabolism. Conversely, the reaction from the baro-receptors to reduced blood pressure is directed primarily to the mobilization of pressor mechanisms.

The secretion of the adrenal medulla is controlled by sympa-thetic fibres in the greater splanchnic nerve. Reflexes from the carotid chemoreceptors would appear to be transmitted to the suprarenal gland by these nerves. Any excitation of the carotid chemoreceptors does not, in fact, induce hyperadrenalinaemia in animals in which the splanchnic nerves have been divided.

We noted in our experiments with carotid chemoreceptor stimulation that when the carotid chemoreceptors were stimulated on either side and the splanchnic nerve was divided or the adrenal gland removed on the same side there were no signs of hyper-adrenalinaemia—no significant increase of blood sugar and no significant pressor reaction, reactions which depend on adrenal secretion. This observation suggested that the reflex from a carotid body travelled mainly to the adrenal gland on the same side.

This view was confirmed in experiments by Fedorchuk (1954). She employed small doses of nicotine (0·2–0·03 mg intravenously) as the stimulus for the carotid chemoreceptors in experiments on decerebrate cats. In these doses nicotine produced excitation of the carotid chemoreceptors but, as control experiments on animals with the carotid bodies removed showed, had no direct stimulating effect on ganglia or suprarenal glands.

These doses of nicotine, injected intravenously, produced a slight rise of blood pressure which was entirely dependent on a reflex from the carotid bodies to the medulla of the suprarenal glands, as it was absent when the sinuses had been denervated and also when the suprarenal glands had been removed or the splanch-nic nerves divided.

In some of the cats the carotid sinus was denervated on one side and the adrenal gland removed on the other in order to determine whether the transmission of the sinus–adrenal reflex was bilateral or mainly ipsilateral. The same doses of nicotine injected intravenously produced no pressor effects in these animals. It was thus proved that the reflex from the carotid bodies was mainly transmitted to the adrenal gland of the same side and, in any case, slight chemoreceptor excitation of short duration did not lead to reflex increase of adrenomedullary secretion on the opposite side.

Carotid body excitation also increases the secretion of glucocorticoid hormones from the cortical layer of the suprarenal glands (Poskalenko, 1958; Ryzhenkov, 1959; Anichkov et al., 1960).

Increase of hormonal activity in the cortical layer of the suprarenal glands has been demonstrated in our laboratory in rats, decerebrate cats and unanaesthetized dogs. The index of the secretory function of the adrenal cortex was ascorbic acid (in the experiments on rats), eosinopenia (in the experiments on decerebrate cats) or the 17-oxycorticosteroids in the blood (experiments on unanaesthetized dogs).

The substances with a selective stimulating action on carotid chemoreceptors that were used are potassium and sodium cyanide, sodium sulphide, nicotine and Corconium (dicholine ester of suberic acid). The results have been described in detail in the chapters on the effects of these substances on the carotid bodies. That reflexes from the carotid receptors were concerned in the increase of adrenocortical secretion observed was proved by the fact that sudden increase was absent or very much reduced after denervation of the sinuses. The adrenocortical reaction in response to carotid chemoreceptor excitation was absent altogether in hypophysectomized animals. The immediate cause of the increase in the secretion of corticosteroids associated with excitation of the carotid chemoreceptors is apparently an increase of ACTH secretion. A short period of carotid chemoreceptor stimulation was followed immediately by increase of 17-hydroxycorticosteroids in the blood of unanaesthetized dogs to one and a half to two times their previous value. Reflexes from the carotid chemoreceptors are, therefore, responsible for considerable increase of ACTH secretion.

17-hydroxycorticosteroids are known to be the most active of the glucocorticoid hormones. They play an important part in the control of carbohydrate metabolism by increasing the glycogen content of the liver and the blood sugar. It is thought that these increases are brought about at the expense of reduction in protein synthesis, or in other words, that increase of energy resources is effected at the expense of reduction in formative processes.

If the purpose of carotid body reflexes is to restore disturbed energy economy, it is perfectly logical that they should be concerned in the reflex secretion of ACTH, which increases the glucocorticoid content of the blood.

Reflex stimulation of ACTH secretion and reflex secretion by the adrenal medulla are observed when the organism is exposed to powerful influences of various kinds, both physical and chemical. The violent reaction of the organism to powerful stimuli is generally regarded as a "stress" reaction (Selye, 1960). This view of the reflex hypersecretion of ACTH is in keeping with its interpretation as a physiological means of mobilizing energy resources.

The reflex hypersecretion of ACTH is a well-known phenomenon, but the paths traversed by the reflexes from the reflexogenic zones to the anterior lobe of the hypophysis have not been adequately clarified. It is generally considered that the reflexes are located in the hypothalamic region, where the centres controlling the secretion of adrenocorticotropic hormone by the anterior lobe of the hypophysis are situated. There is also some fairly convincing evidence that posterior lobe hormones have a stimulating effect on the secretion of ACTH by the anterior lobe. Such findings would indicate that reflex hypersecretion by the posterior lobe leads to increased secretory activity in the anterior lobe and the discharge of adrenocorticotropic hormone into the blood.

It must be remembered in this connexion that all factors (pain, emotion, fear, rage, etc.) that cause hypersecretion of ACTH also induce hypersecretion by the posterior lobe of the hypophysis, particularly of vasopressin, with consequent retardation of water diuresis.

In our laboratory Belous (1952, 1953) has demonstrated that stimulation of the carotid chemoreceptors is followed by reflex retardation of diuresis, caused by hypersecretion from the posterior lobe. Her experiments were carried out on unanaesthetized dogs. The substances used to stimulate the carotid chemoreceptors were hydrocyanic acid, cyanide and acetylcholine. In doses that stimulated the carotid bodies but did not produce pictures of severe poisoning, these substances caused temporary arrest of diuresis. This arrest did not occur in hypophysectomized dogs or in dogs with the carotid sinuses denervated. The conclusion to be drawn from these experiments is that carotid chemoreceptor excitation causes reflex secretion of antidiuretic hormone (vaso-pressin) by the posterior lobe of the hypophysis.

The posterior lobe hypersecretion which develops as a defensive mechanism and as a mobilization of energy resources is in re-sponse to a menacing situation probably primarily to stimulate the secretory function of the anterior hypophyseal lobe and to intensify the secretion of ACTH. In itself, the antidiuretic effect can hardly have great defensive significance, except perhaps when the organism is threatened by disturbance of its osmotic equilibrium.

The discovery that excitation of the carotid chemoreceptors produced a reflex increase of neurohypophyseal secretion raised the question of the pathway for this reflex. The centripetal segment was, of course, the carotid sinus nerve. The most probable suggestion for the centrifugal path is that it runs to the hypophysis from the hypothalamic nuclei in the hypothalamo–hypophyseal tract through the pituitary stalk.

To confirm this the pituitary stalk was divided in three dogs. The operation was carried out by the temporal route under anaesthesia and in conditions of strict asepsis, the dogs being again tested when they had completely recovered from the operation. Nine experiments in which potassium cyanide was injected intra-venously and four experiments in which hydrocyanic gas was inhaled were carried out on these dogs. These experiments gave unexpected results: despite the transection of the pituitary stalk, the cyanide produced antidiuretic effects in these dogs in a very great majority of instances and in many experiments this effect was more powerful than before division of the pituitary stalk (Fig. 32).

The persistence of the antidiuretic effect of hydrocyanic acid and potassium cyanide after division of the pituitary stalk was the result of a reflex from the carotid sinuses. This was proved by experiments on one of the dogs in which the antidiuretic effect produced by breathing hydrocyanic gas or by the intravenous injection of potassium cyanide persisted after division of the pituitary stalk. Both carotid bodies were removed and both carotid sinus nerves were divided in this dog 6 weeks after the operation for division of the pituitary stalk. It was then found that the antidiuretic effect in response to cyanides had disappeared completely.

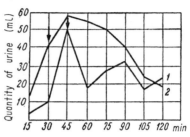

Fig. 32. Dog with chronic fistula of the urinary bladder and the hypophyseal stalk divided. Water test diuresis (40 ml/kg). The arrows indicate the injection of potassium cyanide (0·45 mg/kg). 1—with the carotid sympathetic plexus intact. 2—after removal of the carotid sympathetic plexus, the sinus nerve being intact.

These results showed that the centrifugal part of the arc for the reflex from the carotid bodies to the hypophysis was located mainly in paths other than the hypothalamo–hypophyseal tract and the infundibulum. On the anatomical evidence, this path may be the sympathetic fibres running in the cervical sympathetic nerves through the superior cervical sympathetic ganglion, the carotid sympathetic plexuses and the sympathetic plexus in the circle of Willis, whence branches run to the hypophyseal stalk.

Experiments carried out by A. A. Belous on one of the dogs confirmed that this was the main path over which reflexes from the carotid bodies reached the hypophysis. In this dog the injection of potassium cyanide and the breathing of hydrocyanic gas continued to produce antidiuretic effects after transection of the hypophyseal stalk, which meant that the reflex from the carotid sinuses to the neurohypophysis was still intact. At a subsequent operation on this dog the carotid sympathetic plexuses on both sides were destroyed and the cervical sympathetic nerve was divided on one side. After this supplementary operation, which involved complete denervation of the hypophysis, including the sympathetic pathway, the intravenous injection of potassium cyanide and the breathing of hydrocyanic gas no longer produced antidiuretic effects. As in some experiments the antidiuretic effect of cyanides did not disappear after division of the pituitary stalk and might even be intensified, it can be assumed that the hypophyseal stalk contains fibres which inhibit neurohypophyseal secretion.

All the reflexes originating from the carotid sinuses which we have so far examined are interrelated in physiological significance. The reflexes to the respiratory centre and bronchi increase the effectiveness of respiration, the reflex contraction of the spleen and changes in the lumen of the vessels ensure the transport and proper distribution of the oxygen contained in the blood, and the increased secretion of adrenaline and glucocorticoid hormones mobilize carbohydrates and thus provide the substrate for tissue respiration which is the main source of energy.

Some reflexes observed in connexion with excitation of the carotid chemoreceptors by various substances cannot, however, be classed as reflexes directly increasing the energy stores of the organism. The bradycardia which develops is an example of such a reflex. Yet bradycardia is a very characteristic feature of the reaction developing in response to carotid chemoreceptor excitation.

It must be noted that reflex bradycardia is an exception to the general rule that reflexes from the carotid chemoreceptors are similar in character to the reactions arising in response to fall of blood pressure in the carotid sinuses and opposite in character to those which originate from the carotid baroreceptors when they are stimulated by increase of pressure. Thus, there is intensification of respiration, reflex vasoconstriction and increase of adrenomedullary secretion in response to stimulation of the carotid chemoreceptors. On the other hand, excitation of the carotid baroreceptors produces reflex inhibition of respiration (Moiseyev, 1926), depression of the vasomotor centre and inhibition of adrenomedullary secretion.

It is only in respect to the cardiac rate that reflexes from the chemoreceptors behave similarly to those resulting from baro-receptor excitation. Bradycardia is observed in both cases.

Quite probably this departure from the general rule may have engendered doubt as to whether the bradycardia is actually a direct reflex from the chemoreceptors and not the result of reflex hypertension, or in other words, an indirect consequence of reflexes from the baroreceptors. This doubt was resolved by the preliminary injection of a sympatholytic preparation—sympatho-lytin N,N-dibenzyl-β-bromethylamine (Nazarenko, 1958). There was then no pressor reaction in response to chemoreceptor stimulation and the reflex bradycardia persisted.

Slowing of the heart rate is, therefore, a direct reflex from the carotid chemoreceptors.

The reflex bradycardia resulting from carotid chemoreceptor stimulation is of still further interest in that it indicates that reflexes from the carotid bodies can spread not only over sym-pathetic pathways, which constitute their main lines of trans-mission, but also over parasympathetic paths such as the vagus nerves. Stimulation of the carotid chemoreceptors does not lead to reflex bradycardia in vagotomized and atropinized animals.

The right vagus is known to carry more fibres to the sinus node of the heart than the left vagus and is the main transmitter of impulses slowing the heart rate. On the other hand, it has been demonstrated in our laboratory by Fedorchuk (1954) that reflexes from the carotid bodies to the suprarenal glands are mainly ipsi-lateral.

It seemed probable, therefore, that the same pattern—pre-dominant transmission over an efferent nerve on the same side—would apply,to the reflex from the carotid chemoreceptors to the heart.

Experiments were carried out by Nazarenko (1958) in our laboratory to determine which vagus nerve was mainly concerned in the transmission of reflex slowing of the heart from the two carotid bodies.

The experimental animals were decerebrate cats. As a pre-liminary measure, Sympatholytin (0·08 ml of a 1% solution intravenously) was administered to the animal to exclude pressor reflexes from the baroreceptors which, by increasing blood pressure, might produce baroreceptor reflexes on the heart.

In one series of experiments the cats had the left carotid sinus together with the carotid body and Hering's nerve completely extirpated. One vagus nerve was then divided in the neck; in some experiments the left vagus nerve, i.e. the nerve on the side on which the sinus had been removed, was divided and in some the right nerve, the nerve on the opposite side, was divided. Potassium cyanide was then injected intravenously in the dose usually found sufficient to stimulate the carotid chemoreceptors and invariably produce bradycardia in decerebrate cats with intact sinuses and vagus nerves (0·4–0·6 ml of a 2% solution).

It was found that when the right carotid sinus was retained and the left one removed, the bradycardia in response to the injection of cyanide depended very largely on which vagus nerve was divided. Potassium cyanide produced bradycardia in all five experiments in which the right sinus was intact and the left vagus nerve divided. When the left vagus nerve was intact and the right one divided, that is the nerve on the same side as that on which the sinus was intact, bradycardia was observed in only two of eight experiments. It follows, therefore, that when the right carotid body is stimulated the reflex to the heart is transmitted almost exclusively by the right vagus nerve.

Different results were obtained in a second series of experiments in which the right sinus was removed and one vagus divided. In contrast to what was observed when the sinus and vagus were retained on the right side alone, when both the sinus and the vagus on the left side were retained, bradycardia did not develop from the injection of cyanide in all cases without exception, but only in four of six experiments. Cyanide produced bradycardia with approximately the same frequency when the left sinus was preserved and the right vagus divided (in five of seven experiments). Reflexes from the left carotid sinus can, therefore, be regarded as spreading over both the left and the right vagus nerves. These experiments make it obvious that the transmission of cardiac reflexes from the carotid chemoreceptors is effected over both vagus nerves but that the right vagus nerve is most important in this respect and the left vagus is less important in that it only transmits impulses from the homolateral sinus.

This is in keeping with the known fact that the right vagus nerve is predominant in the transmission of impulses that inhibit the heart. A general comparison of the results of all these experiments has shown, however, that an important factor in determining the efferent path of the reflexes from the carotid chemoreceptors on the heart is the sinus, right or left, from which the reflexes originate. Impulses were conducted predominantly by the vagus nerve on the side on which the sinus was still present.

This applies particularly to impulses conducted by the left vagus nerve, through which reflexes arising from the left and, in rare cases, from the right carotid body were effected.

This difference was less marked in the case of the right vagus which generally transmitted impulse from both right and left sinuses, but even on this side impulses were transmitted in a relatively larger number of cases from the right, the homonymous side.

The ipsilateral paths were thus of slightly greater importance for the transmission of reflexes from the carotid chemoreceptors to the heart.

It is quite probable that inhibitory cardiac reflexes arising from carotid chemoreceptor stimulation are of definite physiological significance although they do not, of course, lead to the mobilization of energy resources.

When cardiac activity is inhibited by the vagus nerves, the expenditure of energy by the cardiac muscle is reduced and consequently catabolic processes proceed at lower levels.

The purpose of the reflex inhibition of the heart that originates from the carotid bodies and that indicates a defective energy metabolism is apparently to ensure economy of the energy resources of the heart as a highly important vital organ.

The reflex inhibition of the motor activity and secretion of the upper regions of the gastro-intestinal tract associated with carotid chemoreceptor stimulation (Startsev, 1958, 1959) can likewise be regarded as a measure to economize energy resources.

The afferent path of all these reflexes is the sinus nerve. Division of this branch of the glossopharyngeal nerve interrupts all reflexes from the carotid body.

The efferent paths of the carotid chemoreceptor reflexes are as varied as the reflexes themselves, which extend to many body functions. Generally, both sympathetic and parasympathetic nerves are used in these paths. The centrifugal part of the arc for reflexes from the carotid bodies to the suprarenal glands, the blood vessels, the intestine, the bronchi, the spleen and the posterior lobe of the hypophysis runs in sympathetic fibres and the cardiac reflexes travel along the vagus nerves, which are parasympathetic.

We have shown earlier that some of these reflexes are predominantly ipsilateral.

Our experimental evidence enables us to draw certain conclusions as to the location of the central part of the reflex arcs arising from the carotid body. These reflexes are retained completely in decerebrate cats and they must, therefore, be located in the brain stem.

Electroencephalography points to increased electrical activity in the brain on stimulation of the carotid receptors (Engel *et al.*, 1944). It is noteworthy that this activity is much more pronounced on the side on which the carotid sinus is stimulated.

Reflexes arising from the carotid chemoreceptors are also represented in the cerebral cortex, a point proved by the conditioned reflex experiments of Belous and Grebenkina (1953).

These experiments were carried out on dogs. Reflexes from the carotid chemoreceptors produced by the action of pharmacological agents—lobeline, cytiton and hydrocyanic acid—were used as unconditioned reactions for establishing conditioned reflexes.

In the series of experiments with lobeline and cytiton the conditioned reflex was elaborated on the basis of the unconditioned respiratory reflex and in the experiments with hydrocyanic acid on the unconditioned reflex secretion of the neurohypophysis.

The experiments of the first series, those in which conditioned reflex dyspnoea was elaborated, were carried out on two dogs. The respiratory movements were recorded kymographically by means of a Marey capsule connected to a cup applied to the animal's thorax. The pharmacological agents selectively stimulating the carotid chemoreceptors (0·4 ml cytiton or 1% lobeline hydrochloride solution) were injected into a subcutaneous vein of the leg six times a week. A metronome, the sound of which served as the conditioning stimulus, was switched on before the injections. The animal developed dyspnoea 5–6 sec after injection of the drug. The metronome was switched off when the dyspnoea produced by the drug ended. In one of the experimental dogs the conditioned reflex was established after forty combinations of injection of the drug with the metronome. On the forty-first experimental day the injection of pure saline intravenously in association with the sound of the metronome produced dyspnoea in this dog. The conditioned reflex became stable in the course of the next few days (Fig. 33).

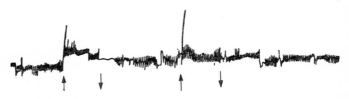

FIG. 33. Dog with an elaborated respiratory conditioned reflex based on the injection of cytiton. Recording of respiration. The arrows pointing upwards indicate the intravenous injection of normal saline and the switching on of the metronome (conditioned stimulus). The arrows pointing downwards indicate the stopping of the metronome.

The conditioned reflex took longer to develop in the other dog and the injection of saline in association with the metronome only began to produce a definite increase in the amplitude of the respiratory movements after 60 combinations of the metronome with the pharmacological agents.

The experiments in which a conditioned antidiuretic reflex was established were carried out on three dogs, the ureters of which had been exteriorized. Before the experiment 350 ml of water were introduced into the dog's stomach. The urine was collected every 15 min for 2 hr. In the control experiments without the drug, diuresis increased gradually, attained its maximum value 60–75 min after the introduction of water, then diminished and had returned to its original level at the end of the second hour. The chemoreceptor stimulus in this series of experiments was hydrocyanic acid, the vapour being inhaled through a mask. The inhalation of hydrocyanic gas produced a well-marked arrest of diuresis in the dogs. As was demonstrated in Belous' experiments, described earlier, this arrest is the result of reflex neurohypophyseal hypersecretion in response to excitation of the carotid chemoreceptors. Experiments were carried out six times a week. Hydrocyanic gas was inhaled once only in each experiment.

Arrest of the conditioned reflex of diuresis could be produced in all three dogs in this series. The conditioning stimulus was the procedure preparing the dog for the inhalation of hydrocyanic acid vapour. A conditioned reflex to application of the mask was formed in two dogs. The application of the mask alone was sufficient to cause arrest of diuresis as early as the eighth experimental day in the case of one of the dogs and on the nineteenth experimental day in another. Previously, this procedure had no effect whatever on diuresis. The conditioned reflex to application of the mask subsequently became stable in both dogs. In the case of the third animal a conditioned reflex was elaborated on the thirty-eighth experimental day. Inhibition of diuresis began to be observed in this dog in response to the application of the cuff for the recording of respiration to its thorax.

Conditioned reflexes could thus be successfully established in all the experimental dogs on the basis of unconditioned reflexes originating from carotid chemoreceptors. In most of the animals the formation of a conditioned reflex required a comparatively large number of combinations of the conditioned stimulus with a drug stimulating the carotid chemoreceptors.

The formation of conditioned reflexes on the basis of unconditioned reflexes is known to proceed relatively slowly from other interoceptors also (Bykov, 1947).

The fact that conditioned reflexes can be formed on the basis of reflexes arising from the carotid chemoreceptors indicates that the control of chemical processes in the tissues, effected through chemoreceptors, is subject to control by the cerebral cortex.

P

References

ABRAHAM, A. (1942) *Acta Univ. Szegediensis* **1**, 1.
ACHESON, G. H. and MOE, G. K. (1945) *J. Pharmacol. Exp. Therap.* **84**, 189.
ACHESON, G. H. and PEREIRA, S. A. (1946) *J. Pharmacol. Exp. Therap.* **87**, 273.
ADO, A. D. and ISHIMOVA, L. M. (1957) *Pathological physiology of allergic reactions* Ed. A. D. ADO. p. 21, Kazan.
ADRIAN, E. D. and BUYTENDIJK (1931) *J. Physiol. (London)* **76**, 121.
ALVERYD, A. and SEM BRODY (1948) *Acta Physiol. Scand.* **15**, 140.
ANICHKOV, S. V. (1934) *Physiol. J. U.S.S.R.* **17**, 1323.
ANICHKOV, S. V. (1936) *Physiol. J. U.S.S.R.* **20**, 73.
ANICHKOV, S. V. (1945) *Bull. Exp. Biol. and Med.* **19**, 75.
ANICHKOV, S. V. (1947) *Physiol. J. U.S.S.R.* **33**, 267.
ANICHKOV, S. V. (1951) *Physiol. J. U.S.S.R.* **37**, 28.
ANICHKOV, S. V. (1952) *Pharmacology of the autonomic nervous system*, pp. 13–20.
ANICHKOV, S. V. (1960) *Pharmacol. and Toxicol.* **23**, 3, 194.
ANICHKOV, S. V. and BELEN'KII, M. L. (1948) *Bull. Exp. Biol. and Med.* **25**, 2, 120.
ANICHKOV, S. V. and GREBENKINA, M. A. (1946) *Bull. Exp. Biol. and Med.* **9**, 22, 3.
ANICHKOV, S. V., ZAKUSOV, V. V., KUZNETSOV, A. I. and POLYAKOV, N. G. (1935). Papers delivered at the 15th International Physiological Congress, Leningrad.
ANICHKOV, S. V., ZAKUSOV, V. V., KUZNETSOV, A. I. and POLYAKOV, N. G. (1936) *Physiol. J. U.S.S.R.* **21**, 809.
ANICHKOV, S. V. and PLESHCHITSER, YA. YA. (1935) *Scientific Papers of the Kirov Military Medical Academy* **4**, 261.
ANICHKOV, S. V. and TOMILINA, T. N. (1950) *Bull. Exp. Biol. and Med.* **30**, 4, 266.
ANICHKOV, S. V. (1926) *Arch. exp. Pathol. Pharmakol. Naunyn-Schmiedeberg's* **118**, 3, 15.
ANICHKOV, S. V. (1935) *Arch. intern. pharmacodynamie* **51**, 4, 36.
ANICHKOV, S. V. (1936) *Arch. intern. pharmacodynamie* **54**, 193.
ANICHKOV, S. V. (1937) *Arch. intern. pharmacodynamie* **55**, 61.
ANICHKOV, S. V. (1953) *Abstr. Comm. XIX Internat. Physiol. Congress* p. 170.
ANICHKOV, S. V. (1959) *XXI Congr. Internat. Ciencias Phisiol. Buenos Aires.*

ANICHKOV, S. V. and KHROMOV-BORISSOV, N. V. (1958) *Atti XI Congresso Soc. Italiana di Anestesiologia* p. 187, Venezia.

ANICHKOV, S. V., MALYGHYNA, E. I., POSKALENKO, A. I. and RYZHENKOV, V. E. (1960) *Arch. intern. pharmacodynamie* 129, 156.

ARBUZOV, S. YA. (1945) *Pharmacol. and Toxicol.* 8, 22.

ARDASHNIKOVA, L. I. (1947) *Résumés of research investigations of the U.S.S.R. Academy of Medical Sciences*, p. 60, Moscow and Leningrad.

ARDASHNIKOVA, L. I. and SHIK, L. L. (1948) *Control of respiration, circulation and gas exchange*, p. 25, Moscow.

ASK-UPMARK, E. (1935) *Acta Psychiat. Scand.* Supp. 6.

ASRATYAN, S. N. (1938a) *Physiol. J. U.S.S.R.* 24, 33.

ASRATYAN, S. N. (1938b) *Scientific papers of the Kirov Military Medical Academy* 17, 229.

ASRATYAN, S. N. and KUZNETSOV, A. I. (1938) *Physiol. J. U.S.S.R.* 24, 5, 964.

ATANACKOVIC, D. (1950) *Arch. intern. pharmacodynamie* 83, 277.

ATANACKOVIC, D. (1951) *Arch. intern. pharmacodynamie* 85, 78.

ATANACKOVIC, D. and DALGAARD-MIKKELSON, S. (1951) *Acta Physiol. Scand.* 22, 77.

AVIADO, D. M., PONTIUS, R. G. and SCHMIDT, C. F. (1949) *J. Pharmacol. Exp. Therap.* 97, 420.

BABAK, E. (1907) *Zbl. Physiol.* 21, 1.

BABAK, E. (1913) *Arch. ges. Physiol. Pflüger's* 154, 66.

BABAK, E. (1921) *Winterstein's Handb. d. vergl. Physiol. Jena* 1, 706.

BABAK, E. and DEDEK, B. (1907) *Arch. ges. Physiol. Pflüger's* 119, 483.

BABSKII, YE. B., GORINEVSKAYA, O. G. and MINAYEV, P. F. (1945) *Bull. Exp. Biol. and Med.* 2, 9, 60.

BALDWIN, E. (1949) *Principles of dynamic biochemistry.* Translation from English Ed. V. A. ENGEL'GARDT. Moscow.

BARGER, G. and DALE, H. H. (1910–1911) *Am. J. Physiol.* 41, 19.

BARRON, G. E. S. and SINGER, T. P. (1945) *J. Biol. Chem.* 157, 221.

BARTELS, H. and WITZLEB E. (1956) *Arch. Ges. Physiol. Pflüger's* 262, 466.

BELEN'KII, M. L. (1948a) *Bull. Exp. Biol. and Med.* 25, 1, 37.

BELEN'KII, K. L. (1948b) *Physiol. J. U.S.S.R.* 34, 113.

BELEN'KII, M. L. (1948c) *Bull. Exp. Biol. and Med.* 25, 2, 116.

BELEN'KII, M. L. (1949c) *Bull. Exp. Biol. and Med.* 26, 4, 297.

BELEN'KII, M. L. (1949b) *Bull. Exp. Biol. and Med.* 28, 7, 64.

BELEN'KII, M. L. (1951a) *Physiol. J. U.S.S.R.* 37, 169.

BELEN'KII, M. L. (1951b) *Trans. of the U.S.S.R. Acad. of Sci.*, New Series, 76, 305.

BELEN'KII, M. L. (1952a) *Pharmacology of the autonomic nervous system*, p. 51, Leningrad.

BELEN'KII, M. L. (1952b) Dissertation. Leningrad.

BELEN'KII, M. L. (1953) *Pharmacology of new therapeutic agents*, p. 116, Leningrad.

BELEN'KII, M. L. and VITOLINYA, M. A. (1954) *Bull. Exp. Biol. and Med.* **5**, 9.

BELEN'KII, M. L. and ROZENGART, V. I. (1949) *Recent Advances in Biol.* **28**, 387.

BELEN'KII, M. L. and STROIKOV, YU. N. (1950) *Bull. Exp. Biol. and Med.* **30**, 358.

BELEN'KII, M. L. and STROIKOV, YU. N. (1952) *Pharmacology of the autonomic nervous system*, p. 51, Leningrad.

BELEN'KII, M. L. and TOMILINA, T. N. (1951) *Trans. of the U.S.S.R. Acad. Sci.* **81**, 961.

BELITSER, V. A. (1939) *Biochemistry* **4**, 498.

BELITSER, V. A. and TSYBAKOVA, YE. T. (1939) *Biochemistry* **4**, 498.

BELOUS, A. A. (1948) *Pharmacol. and Toxicol.* **11**, 3, 26.

BELOUS, A. A. (1950) *Pharmacol. and Toxicol.* **13**, 1, 23.

BELOUS, A. A. (1952) Dissertation. Leningrad.

BELOUS, A. A. (1953) *Pharmacology of new therapeutic agents*, p. 122, Leningrad.

BELOUS, A. A. and GREBENKINA, M. A. (1953) *Physiol. J. U.S.S.R.* **39**, 5, 591.

BERNTHAL, T. (1932) *Am. J. Physiol.* **101**, 6.

BERNTHAL, T. (1934) *Am. J. Physiol.* **109**, 8.

BERNTHAL, T. (1938) *Am. J. Physiol.* **121**, 1.

BERNTHAL, T. and SCHWIND, F. J. (1945) *Am. J. Physiol.* **143**, 361.

BERNTHAL, T. and WEEKS, W. F. (1939) *Am. J. Physiol.* **127**, 94.

BERSIN, T. H. (1935) *Ergeb. Enzymforsch.* **4**, 68.

BETTENCOURT, J. M. (1939) *Presse méd.* **11**, 1557.

BOEKE, J. (1932) *Nerve endings, motor and sensory, in cytology and cellular pathology of the nervous system.* New York.

BOELAERT, R. (1947) *Arch. intern. pharmacodynamie* **63**, 305.

BOELAERT, R. (1948) *Arch. intern. pharmacodynamie* **75**, 417.

BOETTGE, K., JAEGER, K. H. and MITTENZWEI, H. (1957) *Arzneimittel-Forsch.* **1**, 24.

BOOKER, W. M., MOLANO, P. A., FRENCH, D. M. and RHODES, C. J. (1950) *J. Pharmacol. Exp. Therap.* **98**, 107.

BOREI, H. (1939) *Ark. Kemi, Mineralogy och Geologi. Buenos Aires* **23**.

BORODKIN, YU. S., ZAINASHEVA, N. V. and TOMILINA, I. V. (1958) *New therapeutic agents in experimental and clinical use*, p. 163, Leningrad.

BOUKAERT, J. J., DAUTREBANDE, L. and HEYMANS, C. (1931) *Ann. Physiol. physiochim. biol.* **7**, 297.

BOUKAERT, J. J., HEYMANS, C. and SAMAAN, A. (1938) *J. Physiol. physiochim. biol.*, **94**, 4.

BOUKAERT, J. J., GRIMSON, K. S. and HEYMANS, C. (1939) *J. Physiol. physiochim. biol.* **95**, 43.

BOUKAERT, J. J. and PANNIER, R. (1942) *Arch. intern. pharmacodynamie* **67**, 61.

BOVET, D. and BOVET-NITTI, F. (1948) *Structure et activité pharmacodynamique des médicaments du système nerveux végétatif.* Bale, New York.

BOVET, D., BOVET-NITTI, F., GUARINO, S., LONGO, V. G. and MAROTTA, M. (1949) *Rend. ist. super. sanita* **12**, 106.

BOVET, D., BOVET-NITTI, F., GUARINO, S., LONGO, V. and FUSCO, R. (1951) *Arch. intern. pharmacodynamie* **102**, 22.

BOYD, J. D. (1937a) *Contrib. Embryol., Carnegie Inst.* **26**, 1.

BOYD, J. D. (1937b) *Contrib. Embryol., Carnegie Inst.* **152**, 1. Cited by ROSS, L. L., 1959.

BRAUNER, F., BRUCKE, F. and KAINDL, F. (1950) *Arch. intern. pharmacodynamie* **82**, 192.

BRONK, D. W., PITTS, R. F. and LARRABEE, M. G. (1940) *Assoc. Res. Nerv. Dis. Proc.* **20**, 323. Cited by HEYMANS and NEIL, 1958.

BULBRING, E. and BURN, J. H. (1949) *Brit. J. Pharmacol.* **4**, 2, 202; **4**, 3, 245.

BURN, J. H. and DALE, H. H. (1915) *J. Pharmacol. Exp. Therap.* **6**, 417.

BYCK, R. (1957) *Fed. Proc.* **16**, 287.

BYCK, R. (1961) *Brit. J. Pharmacol.* **16**, 15.

BYKOV, K. M. (1947) *Cortex and viscera*, Moscow and Leningrad.

CALDYRO, R. and GARCIA, AUSTT, E. (1949) *Arch. intern. pharmacodynamie* **80**, 89.

CASIER, H. and VLEESCHHOUWER, G. R. (1952) *Arch. intern. pharmacodynamie* **90**, 412.

CELANDER, O. (1954) *Acta physiol. Scand. Suppl.* **32**, 116.

CELESTINO DA COSTA, A. (1944) *Arch. Portug. Sci. Biol.* Suppl. 8. Cited by HEYMANS and NEIL, 1958.

CHAGOVETS, V. YU. (1903) Dissertation. St. Petersburg.

CHERNIGOVSKII, V. N. (1943) *Visceral afferent systems*, Kirov.

CHERNIGOVSKII, V. N. (1947a) *Recent Advances in Biol.* **23**, 215.

CHERNIGOVSKII, V. N. (1947b) *Proc. of 7th All-Union Congress of Physiologists, Biochemists and Pharmacologists*, p. 278.

CHERNIGOVSKII, V. N. (1960) *Interoceptors*, Moscow.

CHIODI, H., DRILL, D. B., CONSOLAZIO, F. and HORVATTI, S. M. (1941) *Am. J. Physiol.* **134**, 683.

CHUNGCHAROEN, D. (1952) Ph.D. Thesis, Univ. of London. Cited by HEYMANS and NEIL, 1958.

CHUNGCHAROEN, D., DALY, M. DE B. and SCHWEITZER, A. (1952a) *J. Physiol.* **117**, 347.

CHUNGCHAROEN, D., DALY, M. DE B. and SCHWEITZER, A. (1952b) *J. Physiol.* **18**, 528.

COMROE, J. H. (JR.) and SCHMIDT, C. F. (1938) *Am. J. Physiol.* **121**, 75.

DALE, H. and LAIDLAW, J. (1910) *J. Physiol.* **41**, 1.

DALY, M. and SCHWEITZER, A. (1951) *Acta Physiol. Scand.* **22**, 66.

DALY, M. DE B., LAMBERSTEN, C. J. and SCHWEITZER, A. (1954) *J. Physiol.* **125**, 67.

DARDYMOV, I. V. and RYBOLOVLEV, R. S. (1955) *Bull. Exp. Biol. and Med.* **40**, 11, 41.

DAUTREBANDE, L. and MARECHAL, C. (1933) *Compt. rend. soc. biol.* **113**, 76.

DAUTREBANDE, L. and PHILLIPOT, E. (1935) *Compt. rend. soc. biol.* **20**, 1371.

DE BOISSEZON, P. (1943) *Biol. Méd.* **33**, 34.

DE BOISSEZON, P. (1944) *Bull. histol. appl. et tech. microscop.* **21**, 54.

DE CASTRO, F. (1926) *Trav. Lab. Recherches Biol. Univ. Madrid* **24**, 342–365.

DE CASTRO, F. (1927–1928) *Trav. Lab. Recherches Biol. Univ. Madrid* **25**, 331.

DE CASTRO, F. (1940) *Trav. Lab. Recherches Biol. Univ. Madrid* **3**, 297.

DE CASTRO, F. (1944) *Trav. Lab. Recherches Biol. Univ. Madrid* **36**, 345.

DE CASTRO, F. (1951) *Acta Physiol. Scand.* **22**, 14–43.

DE KOCK, L. L. (1951) *Nature* **167**, 611.

DE KOCK, L. L. (1954) *Acta Anat.* **21**, 101.

DELAUNOIS, F. L. and MARTINI, L. (1953) *Arch. intern. pharmacodynamie* **94**, 430.

DENISENKO, P. P. (1958) *Gangliolytics and agents blocking neuromuscular synapses*, p. 21, Leningrad.

DE WISPELEARE, M. (1936) *Compt. rend. soc. biol.* **124**, 276.

DE WISPELEARE, H. (1937) *Arch. intern. pharmacodynamie* **56**, 363.

DICKENS, F. (1941) *Die Methoden der Fermentforschung.* Vol. 3, 2425. Leipzig.

DIXON, W. E. (1924) *Heffter's Handb. der Experimentellen Pharmakologie*, p. 656, Berlin.

DONTAS, A. S. (1955) *J. Pharmacol. Exp. Therap.* **115**, 1, 46.

DOUGLAS, W. (1952a) *J. Physiol.* **117**, 71.

DOUGLAS, W. (1952b) *J. Physiol.* **118**, 373.

DOUGLAS, W. and TOH, J. (1952c) *J. Physiol.* **117**, 71.

DOUGLAS, W. and GRAY, J. A. B. (1953) *J. Physiol.* **119**, 118.

DRIPPS, R. D. and COMROE (JR.), J. H. (1944) *Am. J. Med. Sci.* **208**, 681.

DRIPPS, R. D. and COMROE, J. H. (1947) *Am. J. Physiol.* **149**, 277.

DRIPPS, R. D. and DUMKE, P. R. (1943) *J. Pharmacol. Exp. Therap.* **77**, 290.

DUBININ, F. G. (1937) *Arch. of Biological Sciences* **46**, 47.

DUKE, H., GREEN, J. H. and NEIL, E. J. (1953) *J. Physiol.* **118**, 520.

DUMKE, P. R., SCHMIDT, C. F. and CHIODI, H. P. (1941) *Am. J. Physiol.* **133**, 1.

ECKER, A. and WIEDERSHEIM, R. (1896) *Anatomie des Frosches, bearb. v. Ernst Gaupp.*, Braunschweig.

ELLIS, M. M. (1919) *Am. J. Physiol.* **50**, 267.

ENDERS, A. and SCHMIDT, L. (1952) *Arch. intern. pharmacodynamie* **91**, 157.

ENGEL, G. L., ROMANO and McLIN, T. R. (1944) *Arch. Int. Med.* **74** (2).

ENGELHARDT, V. A. (1930) *Proc. of 4th All-Union Congress of Physiologists*, p. 275, Kharkov.

ENGELHARDT, V. A. (1941) *Recent Advances in Biol.* **14**, 177.

ENGELHARDT, V. A. (1948) *Proceedings of Conference on large-molecule compounds* p. 122. Moscow and Leningrad.

ENGELHARDT, V. A. and BRAUNSHTEIN, A. YE. (1928) *Bull. Exp. Biol. and Med.* **8**, 22, 162.

ENGELHARDT, V. A. and LYUBIMOVA, M. N. (1942) *Biochemistry* **7**, 205.

ENGELHARDT, V. A. and SHAPOT, V. S. (1935) *Proc. of 10th International Physiological Congress*, 471.

ENGELHARDT, V. (1932) *Biochem. Z.* **251**, 343.

EULER, U. S. v. (1938) *Scand. Arch. Physiol.* **80**, 94.

EULER, U. S. v. and LILJESTRAND, G. (1934) *Scand. Arch. Physiol.* **71**, 73.

EULER, U. S. v. and LILJESTRAND, G. (1936) *Scand. Arch. Physiol.* **74**, 101.

EULER, U. S. v. and LILJESTRAND, G. (1940) *Acta Physiol. Scand.* **1**, 93.

EULER, U. S. v. and LILJESTRAND, G. (1941) *Acta Physiol. Scand.* **2**, 1.

EULER, U. S. v., LILJESTRAND, G. and ZOTTERMANN, Y. (1939) *Scand. Arch. Physiol.* **83**, 132.

EULER, U. S. v., LILJESTRAND, G. and ZOTTERMANN, Y. (1941) *Acta Physiol. Scand.* **1**, 383.

FABIANII, M. and SZEBEHELYI, (1948) *Arch. intern. pharmacodynamie* **76**, 397.

FARBER, S. (1936) *Arch. intern. pharmacodynamie* **53**, 377.

FEDORCHUK, YE. S. (1954) *Bull. Exp. Biol. and Med.* **6**, 7.

FEDORCHUK, YE. S. (1956) *Recent findings in the physiology of the motor apparatus in the normal state and in poliomyelitis*, p. 360, Leningrad.

FEDORCHUK, YE. S. (1957). Dissertation. Leningrad.

FERNANDEZ, A. (1949) *Arch. intern. pharmacodynamie* **80**, 82.

FOLKOW, B. (1952) *Acta Physiol. Scand.* **25**, 49.

GADDUM, J. H. and LEMBERG, K. (1949) *Brit. J. Pharmacol.* **4**, 4, 401.

GARNER, C. M. and DUNCAN, D. (1958) *Anat. Rec.* **130**, 691.

GAVA, M. and RASKOVA, H. (1960) *Physiol. Bohemosloven* **9**, 122.

GAYET, R. and QUIVY, D. (1934) *Compt. rend. soc. biol.* **115**, 115.

GERNANDT, B. E. (1946) *Acta Physiol. Scand.* **11**, suppl. 35.

GESELL, R. (1939) *Ann. Rev. Physiol.* **1**, 185.

GESELL, R. and HANSEN, E. T. (1945) *Am. J. Physiol.* **144**, 126.

GINZEL, K. H. and KOTTEGODA, S. R. (1954) *J. Physiol.* **123**, 277.

GOORMAGHTIGH, N. and PANNIER, R. (1939) *Arch. Biol.* **50**, 455.

GORDIYENKO, A. N. and NAZAROVA, T. A. (1944) *Pharmacol. and Toxicol.* **7**, 3, 23.

GREBENKINA, M. A. (1950) Dissertation. Leningrad.

GREBENKINA, M. A. (1952) *Pharmacology of the autonomic nervous system*, p. 95, Leningrad.

HAAG, H. B. (1933) *J. Pharmacol. Exp. Therap*, **48**.

HANDOVSKY, H. (1934) *Compt. rend. soc. biol.* **17**, 238.

HAUSS, W. H. and SHEN, T. (1939) *Arch. intern. pharmacodynamie* **62**, 4, 461.

HAUSS, W. H., KREUZIGER, H. and ASTEROTH, H. (1949) **38**, 28.

HERING, H. (1924) *Münch. med. Wochschr.* **22**, 701.

HEUBNER, W. (1913) *Arch. Exp. Pharmacol.* **72**, 241.

HEYMANS, C. (1941) *Schweiz. Med. Wochschr.* **11**, 285.

HEYMANS, C. (1951) *Acta Physiol. Scand.* **22** (1), **4**.
HEYMANS, C. (1955) *Pharmacol. Rev.* **7**, 119.
HEYMANS, C. and BOUCKAERT, J. J. (1930) *J. Physiol* **69**, 254.
HEYMANS, C. and BOUCKAERT, J. J. (1941) *Arch. intern. pharmacodynamie* **65**, 196.
HEYMANS, C., BOUCKAERT, J. J. and DAUTREBANDE, L. (1930) *Arch. intern. pharmacodynamie* **39**, 400.
HEYMANS, C., BOUCKAERT, J. J. and DAUTREBANDE, L. (1931a) *Compt. rend. soc. biol.* **106**, 52.
HEYMANS, C., BOUCKAERT, J. J. and DAUTREBANDE, L. (1931b) *Compt. rend. soc. biol.* **106**, 54.
HEYMANS, C., BOUCKAERT, J. J. and DAUTREBANDE, L. (1931c) *Compt. rend. soc. biol.* **106**, 1276.
HEYMANS, C., BOUCKAERT, J. J. and DAUTREBANDE, L. (1931d) *Arch. intern. pharmacodynamie* **40**, 54.
HEYMANS, C., BOUCKAERT, J. J. and DAUTREBANDE, L. (1931e) *Compt. rend. soc. biol.* **106**, 1279.
HEYMANS, C., BOUCKAERT, J. J. and DAUTREBANDE, L. (1932) *Compt. rend. soc. biol.* **109**, 566.
HEYMANS, C., BOUCKAERT, J. J., EULER, U. S. v. and DAUTREBANDE, L. (1932) *Arch. intern. pharmacodynamie* **43**, 86.
HEYMANS, C., BOUCKAERT, J. J., FARBER, S. and HSU, F. J. (1936) *Arch. intern. pharmacodynamie* **54**, 129.
HEYMANS, C., BOUCKAERT, J. J. and HANDOVSKY, H. (1935) *Compt. rend. soc. biol.* **119**, 542.
HEYMANS, C., BOUCKAERT, J. J. and PANNIER, R. (1944) *Bull. Acad. Méd. Roumanie* **9**, 42. Cited by HEYMANS and NEIL, 1958.
HEYMANS, C., BOUCKAERT, J. J. and REGNIERS, P. (1933) *Le sinus carotidien et la zone homologue cardio–aortique*, Paris.
HEYMANS, C., DELAUNOIS, A. L., MARTINI, L. and JANSSEN, P. (1953) *Arch. intern. pharmacodynamie* **96**, 209.
HEYMANS, C. and HEUVEL-HEYMANS, G. VAN DEN (1953) *Arch. intern. pharmacodynamie* **93**, 95.
HEYMANS, C. and NEIL, E. (1958) *Reflexogenic areas of the cardiovascular system*, London.
HEYMANS, C. and RIJLANT, P. (1933) *Compt. rend. soc. biol.* **113**, 69.
HEYMANS, C. and VLEESCHHOUWER, C. B. (1950) *Arch. intern. pharmacodynamie* **84**.
HEYMANS, C., VLEESCHHOUWER, G. B. DE and HEUVEL-HEYMANS, G. VAN DEN (1951) *Arch. intern. pharmacodynamie* **85**, 188.
HEYMANS, J. F. and HEYMANS, C. (1926) *Arch. intern. pharmacodynamie* **32**, 1.
HOFFMAN, H. and BIRREL, G. H. W. (1958) *Acta Anat.* **32**, 297.
HOLLINSHEAD, W. H. (1943) *Am. J. Anat.* **73**, 185.
HOLLINSHEAD, W. H. and SAWYER, C. H. (1945) *Am. J. Physiol.* **144**, 79.
HOLTZ, P. and SCHUMANN, H. J. (1949) *Arch. Exp. Path. Pharmak.* **206**, 49.

HOUSSAY, B. A. and MOLINELLI, E. A. (1925) *Compt. rend. soc. biol.* **93**, 1124.

HUNT, R. (1926) *J. Pharmacol. Exp. Therap.* **23**, 376.

ISHIMOVA, L. M. (1947) *Pathological physiology of allergic reactions.* Ed. A. D. ADO KAZAN; (1948) *Bull. Exp. Biol. and Med.* **2**, 122.

IVANOV, G. F. (1930) *Chromaffin and interrenal system in man*, Moscow.

IVANOV, I. I. (1950) *Chemical dynamics of muscles and motile cells*, Medgiz, Moscow.

JARISCH, A., LANDGREN, S., NEIL, E. and ZOTTERMAN, G. (1952) *Acta Physiol. Scand.* **25**, 195.

KAINDL, F. and WERNER, G. (1948) *Arch. intern. pharmacodynamie* **205**.

KARASIK, V. M. (1930) *Russian Physiol. J.* **13**, 525.

KARASIK, V. M. (1934) *Physiol. J. U.S.S.R.* **17**, 600.

KARASIK, V. M. (1948) *Bull. Exp. Biol. and Med.* **26**, 229.

KARLIK, L. N. (1939) *The hypophysis in physiology and pathology*, Moscow.

KEILIN, D. (1936) *Proc. Roy. Soc. B.* **121**, 165.

KETY, S. S. and SCHMIDT, C. F. (1945) *Am. J. Physiol.* **143**, 53.

KETY, S. S. and SCHMIDT, C. F. (1948) *J. Clin. Invest.* **27**, 484.

KOCH, E. (1931) *Die reflektorische Selbststeuerung des Kreislaufes. Steinkopff*, Leipzig.

KOELLE, G. B. (1950) *J. Pharmacol. Exp. Therap.* **100**, 158.

KOELLE, G. B. (1951) *J. Pharmacol. Exp. Therap.* **103**, 153.

KOSHTOYANTS, KH. S. (1945) *Jubilee Meeting of the U.S.S.R. Academy of Sciences*, 15 June–3 July 1945, **2**, 419. Moscow and Leningrad.

KOSHTOYANTS, KH. S. (1947) *Collection marking the 30th anniversary of the Great October Socialist Revolution*, **2**, 437. Moscow and Leningrad.

KOSHTOYANTS, KH. S. (1948) *Trans. of the U.S.S.R. Acad. Sci.* **60**, 1105.

KOSHTOYANTS, KH. S. (1950a) *Physiol. J. U.S.S.R.* **36**, 92.

KOSHTOYANTS, KH. S. (1950b) *Trans. of the U.S.S.R. Acad. Sci.* **72**, 981.

KOSHTOYANTS, KH. S. (1950c) *Principles of comparative physiology*, Vol. 1. U.S.S.R. Acad. Sci. Press, Moscow and Leningrad.

KOSHTOYANTS, KH. S. (1951) *Proteins, metabolism and nervous control*, U.S.S.R. Acad. Sci. Press, Moscow.

KOSHTOYANTS, KH. S. and LOGUNOVA, K. S. (1950) *Trans. of the U.S.S.R. Acad. Sci.* **73**, 429.

KOSHTOYANTS, KH. S. and MOGORAS, S. S. (1946) *Trans. of the U.S.S.R. Acad. Sci.* **54**, 461.

KOSHTOYANTS, KH. S. and TURPAYEV, T. M. (1946) *Trans. of the U.S.S.R. Acad. Sci.* **54**, 181.

KRAVCHINSKII, B. D. (1945) *Physiol. J. U.S.S.R.* **31**, 11.

KRASNOVSKAYA, L. A. (1941) *Arch. of Biol. Sci.* **64**, 46.

KRASNOVSKAYA, L. A. (1943) *Bull. Exp. Biol. and Med.* **16**, 16.

KRAYER, O. (1958) *Pharmacology in medicine*, New York.

KRAYER, O. and ACHESON, G. H. (1946) *Physiol. Rev.* **26**, 383.

KROGH, A. (1904) *Scand. Arch. Physiol.* **15**, 328.

KROGH, A. (1941) *Comparative physiology of respiratory mechanisms.* Oxford University Press, London.

KRYLOV, S. S. (1956) *Physiol. J. U.S.S.R.* **42**, 8, 723.

KUDRIN, A. P. (1950) *Pharmacol. and Toxicol.* **13**, 37.

KUNO, Y. and BRUCKE, E. T. (1914) *Arch. ges. Physiol.* **157**, 117.

KUZNETSOV, A. I. (1928) *Bull. Exp. Biol. and Med.* **10**, 266.

KUZNETSOV, A. I. (1938) *Scientific papers of the Kirov Military Medical Academy* **17**, 121.

LANDGREN, S. and NEIL, E. (1951) *Acta Physiol. Scand.* **23**, 152, 158.

LANDGREN, S., LILJESTRAND, G. and ZOTTERMAN, Y. (1952) *Acta Physiol. Scand.* **26**, 2, 264.

LANDGREN, S., LILJESTRAND, G. and ZOTTERMAN, Y. (1953) *Arch. exp. Pathol. Pharmakol.* **219**, 185.

LANDGREN, S., LILJESTRAND, G. and ZOTTERMAN, Y. (1954) *Acta Physiol. Scand.* **30**, 2, 149.

LANDGREN, S., NEIL, E. and ZOTTERMAN, Y. (1952) *Acta Physiol. Scand.* **25**, 24.

LANGLEY, J. N. and DICKINSON W. L. (1889) *Proc. Roy. Soc.* **46**, 423.

LANGLEY, J. N. and DICKINSON, W. L. (1890) *J. Physiol.* **11**, 509.

LAUER, N. V. (1949) *Hypoxia (Gipoksiya)* **84**, Ukr. SSR Acad. Sci. Press, Kiev.

LAVES, W. (1956) *Münch. Med. Wochschr.* **98**, 1.

LAVRENT'YEV, B. I. (1943) *J. General Biol.* **4**, 232.

LE MESSERIER, H. (1936) *J. Pharmacol.* **57**, 438.

LEHMANN, H. (1935) *Biochem. Z.* **281**, 271.

LEVER, J. D. and BOYD, J. D. (1957) *Nature* **179**, 1082.

LIKHACHEV, A. A. (1931) *Protection in chemical warfare*, p. 68, Moscow.

LILLENTHAL, J. L. (JR.) (1950) *J. Pharmacol. Exp. Therap.* **99**, 324.

LILJESTRAND, G. (1949) *Acta Physiol. Scand.* **18**, 243.

LILJESTRAND, G. (1951) *Acta Physiol. Scand.* **24**, 225.

LILJESTRAND, G. (1952) *R. C. Inst. Sup. Sanita* **25**, 1242.

LILJESTRAND, G. (1953) *Acta Physiol. Scand.* **29**, 74.

LILJESTRAND, G. (1954) *Pharm. Rev.* **6**, 1, 73.

LIPMAN, F. (1929a) *Verh. Deutsch. Pharmakol. Gesellschaft*, 9-te Tagung.

LIPMAN, F. (1929b) *Biochem. Z.* **206**, 171.

LIPMAN, F. (1941) *Advances in Enzymol.* **1**, 99.

LOOMIS, W. F. and LIPMAN, F. (1948) *J. Biol. Chem.* **173**, 807.

LYUBIMOVA, M. P. and ENGEL'GARDT, V. A. (1939) *Biochemistry* **4**, 716.

MACCLURE, F. J. (1949) *Ann. Rev. Biochem.* **18**, 335.

MACHT, D. I. (1917) *J. Pharmacol. Exp. Therap.* **9**, 197; cited by NIMS et al., 1953.

MALMEJAC, J. (1959) *XXI Internat. Congress of Physiological Sciences*, Buenos Aires. Symposia and special lectures, 132.

MALYGINA, YE. I. (1961) *Problems of Endocrinol. and Hormonotherapy* **2**, 3.

MARRI, R. and RINDI, V. (1940) *Arch. Fisiol.* **40**, 438.

MARSHAK, M. YE. (1948) *7th All-Union Congress of Physiologists, Biochemists and Pharmacologists* 5, Moscow.

MARSHALL, A. M. (1893) *Vertebrate embryology*, London.

MARSHALL, E. K. (JR.) and ROSENFELD, M. J. (1935) *J. Pharmacol. Exp. Therap.* **54**, 155.

MARSHALL, E. K. and ROSENFELD, M. J. (1936) *J. Pharmacol. Exp. Therap.* **57**, 437.

MARTINI, L. and ROVATI, V. (1954) *Arch. intern. pharmacodynamie* **97**, 420.

MARTINI, L. and CALLIAUW, L. (1955) *Arch. intern. pharmacodynamie* **101**: 1, 49.

MASHKOVSKII, M. D. (1941) *Pharmacol. and Toxicol.* **4**, 1, 34.

MASHKOVSKII, M. D. (1943) *Pharmacol. and Toxicol.* **6**, 2.

MASHKOVSKII, M. D. and RABKINA, L. YE. (1952) *Pharmacol. and Toxicol.* **15**, 2, 23.

MATUO, K. (1940) *Fukuoka Acta Med.* **33**, 33.

MAURER, F. (1888) *Gegenbauer's Morphologisches Jahrbuch* **14**, 175.

MAZELLA, H. and MIGLIARO, E. (1949) *Arch. intern. pharmacodynamie* **80**, 79.

MEDNIKYAN, G. A. (1936) *Arch. of Biol. Sci.* **41**, 113.

MEDNIKYAN, G. A. and ASRATYAN, S. N. (1951) *Pharmacol. and Toxicol.* **14**, 2, 39.

MEI LING, H. A. (1938) *Acta Neerl. Morphol.* **1**, 193.

MEL'NIKOVA, T. A. (1947) Dissertation. Leningrad.

MEL'NIKOVA, T. A. (1952) *Pharmacology of the autonomic nervous system*, 68, Leningrad.

MERCIER, F. and DELPHAUT, J. (1934a) *Compt. rend. soc. biol.* **116**, 1039.

MERCIER, F., RIZZIO, C. and DELPHAUT, J. (1934b) *Compt. rend. soc. biol.* **115**, 546.

MEYER, F. (1927) *Arch. Ges. Physiol.* **215**, 545.

MEYER, H. (1935) *Z. Vergleich. Physiol.* **22**, 435.

MEYERHOF, O. (1944) *Ann. N.Y. Acad. Sci.* **45**, 357.

MITROFANOV, A. I. (1957) *Bull. Exp. Biol. and Med.* **7**, 60.

MIKHEL'SON, M. YA., RYBOLOVLEV, R. S., GORELIK, A. M. and DARDYMOV, I. V. (1957) *The physiological role of acetylcholine and the discovery of new therapeutic agents*, p. 363. Ed. M. YA. MIKHEL'SON, Leningrad.

MIKHEL'SON, M. YA., SAVATEYEV, N. V., ROZHKOVA, YE, K. and LUKOMSKAYA, N. YA. (1957) *The physiological role of acetylcholine and the discovery of new therapeutic agents*, p. 25, Leningrad.

MOE, G. K., CAPO, L. R. and PERALTA, B. R. (1948) *Am. J. Physiol.* **153**, 601.

MOISSEIEFF, E. (1926) *Z. Exp. Med.* **53**, 696.

MULINOS, M. G. and ATHENEOS, J. (1932) *J. Pharmacol. Exp. Therap.* **65**, 269.

MULLER and STEFENSON, (1937) *Scand. Arch. Physiol.* **76**, 115.

NAZARENKO, M. A. (1958) *Jubilee collection of papers by junior scientists of LSGMI*, Leningrad.

NEKHOROSHEV, N. P. (1948) *Recent Advances in Biol.* **25**, 3, 451.
NIKIFOROWSKY, P. M. (1912–1913) *J. Physiol.* **45**, 459.
NIMS, R. G., SEVERINGHAUS, J. and COMROE, J. H. (JR.) (1953) *J. Pharmacol. Exp. Therap.* **109**, 1, 58.
OLTHOFF, H. (1934) *Z. Vergleich. Physiol.* **21**, 534.
ORBELI, L. A. and MIKHEL'SON, A. A. (1937) *Physiol. J. U.S.S.R.* **23**, 168.
OREKHOV, A. P. (1921) *Ber. Deut. chem. ges.* **64**.
OWEN, H. and GESELL, R. (1931) *Proc. Soc. Exp. Biol.* **28**, 765.
PAL'GOVA, L. YE. and VOLOBUYEV, V. I. (1940) *Bull. Exp. Biol. and Med.* **10**, 454.
PALME, F. (1934) *Z. Mikroskop. Anat. Forsch.* **36**, 391.
PANNIER, R. and BACKER, J. DE (1945) *Arch. intern. pharmacodynamie* **70**, 110.
PASKOV, D. S. (1958) Dissertation. Leningrad.
PATON, W. D. and ZAIMIS, M. (1948) *Nature* **162**, 716.
PATON, W. D. and ZAIMIS, J. (1949) *Brit. J. Pharmacol.* **4**, 381.
PETROPAVLOVSKAYA, A. A. (1953) *Pharmacology of new therapeutic agents,* Leningrad.
PHILLIPOT, R. (1937) *Arch. intern. pharmacodynamie* **57**, 357.
PICKFORD, M. (1939) *J. Physiol.* **95**, 1, 226.
POLOSUKHIN, A. P. (1947) *7th All-Union Congress of Physiologists, Biochemists and Pharmacologists.*
POLUEKTOV, M. N. (1935) *Bull. Inst. Exp. Med.* **8**, 8.
POLUEKTOV, M. N. (1946) **9**, 5, 8.
POLYAKOV-STANEVICH, N. G. (1938a) *Scientific Papers of the Kirov Military Medical Academy* **17**, 143.
POLYAKOV-STANEVICH, N. G. (1938b) *Physiol. J. U.S.S.R.* **24**, 986.
POLYAKOV-STANEVICH, N. G. (1938c) *Bull. Exp. Biol. and Med.* **5**, 4, 376.
POPOV, N. A. and EGOLINSKII, YA. A. (1929) *Russian Physiol. J.* **12**, 97.
POSKALENKO, A. N. (1955) *Problems of Endocrinol. and Hormonotherapy* **1**, 5, 92.
POSKALENKO, A. N. (1958) *Problems of Endocrinol. and Hormonotherapy* **4**, 1, 46.
RAISKINA, M. YE. (1951) *Pharmacol. and Toxicol.* **14**, 1, 31.
RASKOVA, H., FLAVOVA, O. and RYBOVA, B. (1956) *Arch. Exp. Path. Pharmak.* **228**, 145.
RASPOPOVA, G. V. (1955) *Pharmacol. and Toxicol.* **18**, 1, 37.
ROSS, L. L. (1957) *Anat. Rec.* **129**, 4, 433.
ROSS, L. L. (1959) *J. Biophys. Biochem. Cytol.* **6**, 253.
ROSS, L. and HUNT, T. E. (1954) *Anat. Rec.* **118**, 436.
ROZANOVA, V. D. (1947) *7th All-Union Congress of Physiologists, Biochemists and Pharmacologists,* p. 699.
RUNNSTROM, L., BOREI, H. and SPERBER, E. (1939) *Arkiv Kemi, Mineral. Geol. Buenos Aires* **176**, 460.
RYBOLOVLEV, R. S. *Physiological role of acetylcholine and the discovery of new therapeutic agents.* p. 322, Ed. M. YA. MIKHEL'SON. Leningrad.

RYZHENKOV, V. YE. (1959) *Problems of Endocrinol. and Hormonotherapy* **5**, 6, 19.

SAKSONOV, P. P. (1946) *Pharmacol. and Toxicol.* **9**, 5, 13.

SAKUSSOW, W. W. (1934) *Arch. Exp. Pathol. Pharmakol.* **176**, 460.

SAMAAN, A. and STELLA, G. (1935) *J. Physiol.* **85**, 309.

SARGIN, S. D. (1934) *The chemico-pharmaceutical industry*, Moscow.

SAYERS, M., SAYERS, G. and WOODBURY, I. (1948) *Endocrinology* **42**, 379.

SCHMIDT, C. F. (1932a) *Am. J. Physiol.* **101**, 91.

SCHMIDT, C. F. (1932b) *Am. J. Physiol.* **102**, 119.

SCHMIDT, C. F. (1940) *J. Lab. Clin. Med.* **26**, 223.

SCHMIDT, C. F. (1944) *Anaesthesiology* **5**, 77.

SCHMIDT, C. F. and COMROE, J. H. (JR.) (1940) *Physiol. Rev.* **20**, 115.

SCHMIDT, C. F., COMROE, J. H. (JR.) and DRIPPS, R. D. (JR.) (193) *Proc. Soc. Exp. Biol.* **42**, 31.

SCHMIDT, C. F. (1956) Chapter on "Respiration" in *McLeod's physiology in modern medicine.* Ed. P. BARD. London

SCHMIDT, C. F., DUMKE, P. L. and DRIPPS, R. D. (1939) *Am. J. Physiol.* **128**, 1.

SCHWEITZER, A. and WRIGHT, S. (1938) *Quart. J. Exp. Physiol.* **28**, 33.

SEITS, I. F. and ENGEL'GARDT, V. A. (1949a) *Trans. of the U.S.S.R. Acad. Sci.* **66**, 439.

SEITS, I. F. and ENGEL'GARDT, V. A. (1949b) *Biochemistry* **14**, 487.

SELYE, H. (1960) *Features of the adaptation syndrome.* Russian translation, Moscow.

SEPP, YE. K. (1949) *History of the development of the vertebrate nervous system*, Moscow.

SHAPOT, V. S. (1945) *Biochemistry* **10**, 45.

SHEN, T. C. R. and HAUSS, W. H. (1939) *Arch. intern. pharmacodynamie* **63**, 251.

SHIK, L. L. (1949) *Hypoxia* **46**. Kiev.

SMIRNOV, A. A. (1944) *Collection of scientific papers of VMMA* **3** (2), 81.

SMIRNOV, A. A. (1945) *The carotid reflexogenic zone*, Leningrad.

SMYTH, D. H. (1937) *J. Physiol.* **88**, 425.

SMYTH, D. H. (1939) *J. Physiol.* **95**, 305.

SNYDER, F. F. and ROSENFELD, M. (1936) *Am. J. Physiol.* **116**, 147.

SNYDER, F. F. and ROSENFELD, M. (1937) *Am. J. Physiol.* **119**, 153.

SORENI, E. T. and DEGTYAREV, R. G. (1948) *Ukrain. Biochem. J.* **20**, 250.

SOSKIN, S. and LEVIN, R. (1946) *Carbohydrate metabolism. Correlation of physiological, biochemical and clinical aspects*, Univ. of Chicago Press, Chicago.

STARTSEV, V. G. (1958) *Physiol. J. U.S.S.R.* **44**, 1, 29.

STARTSEV, V. G. (1959) *Physiol. J. U.S.S.R.* **45**, 1. 83.

SYRNEVA, YU. I. (1938) *Pharmacol. and Toxicol.* **1**, 1, 27.

SZENT-GYORGYI, A. (1960) *Bioenergetics.* Russian translation, Moscow.

THOMPSON, R. H. S. (1946) *Biochem. J.* **40**, 525.

TOMILINA, T. N. (1951) Dissertation. Leningrad.

TOMILINA, T. N. (1952) *Pharmacology of the autonomic nervous system*, p. 20, Moscow and Leningrad.

TRENDELENBURG, P. (1923) *Heffter's Handb. d. exp. Pharmakologie* 1, 470, 564, Berlin.

TSIRK, K. V. (1957) *Physiological role of acetylcholine and the discovery of new therapeutic agents.* Ed. M. YA. MIKHEL'SON, Leningrad.

UR'YEVA, F. I. and SHIK, L. L. (1940) *Arch. of Biol. Sci.* 57, 55.

VAN DAM, L. (1938) *On the utilization of oxygen and the regulation of breathing in some aquatic animals.* Volharding, Groningen. Cited by HEYMANS and NEIL, 1958.

VEDENEYEVA, Z. I. (1951) *Physiol. J. U.S.S.R.* 37, 6, 732.

VELASQUEZ, L. (1941) *Medicina* 9, 292.

VERBEKE, R. (1949a) *Arch. intern. pharmacodynamie* 79, 1.

VERBEKE, R. (1949b) *Arch. intern. pharmacodynamie* 80, 19.

VERBEKE, R. and VOTAVA, Z. (1949) *Arch. intern. pharmacodynamie* 79, 367.

VERDONK, A. (1937) *Compt. rend. soc. biol.* 126, 431.

VERDONK, A. (1939) *Arch. intern. pharmacodynamie* 63, 376.

VERDONK, A. (1941) *Arch. intern. pharmacodynamie* 65, 111.

VINIKOVA, B. G. (1950) *Physiol. J. U.S.S.R.* 36, 723.

VINIKOVA, B. G. (1952) *Pharmacology of the autonomic nervous system*, p. 77, Leningrad.

VISHNYAKOV, S. M. (1952) *Pharmacol. and Toxicol.* 15, 3, 14.

VISHNYAKOV, S. M., MIKHEL'SON, M. YA., ROZHKOVA, YE. K. and RYBOLOVLEV, R. S. (1952) *Bull. Exp. Biol. and Med.* 23, 3, 52.

VOLOKHOV, A. A. and OBRAZTSOVA, G. A. (1950) *Physiol. J. U.S.S.R.* 36, 545.

WANG, S. C., NGAI, S. H. and GROSSMAN, R. G. (1954) *J. Pharmacol. Exp. Therap.* 110, 51.

WARBURG, O. (1946) *Schwermetalle als Wirkungsgruppen von Fermenten*, Berlin.

WARBURG, O. (1948) *Fluoridhemmung der Enolasein Wasserstoffübertragende Fermente*, p. 49, Berlin.

WINDER, C. V. (1937) *Am. J. Physiol.* 118, 389.

WINDER, C. V. (1939) *Am. J. Physiol.* 126, 655.

WINDER, C. V. (1942) *Am. J. Physiol.* 136, 200.

WINDER, C. V. and WINDER, H. O. (1933) *Am. J. Physiol.* 105, 337.

WINDER, C. V., BERNTHAL, T. and WEEKS, W. F. (1938a) *Am. J. Physiol.* 123, 15.

WINDER, C. V., BERNTHAL, T. and WEEKS, W. F. (1938b) *Am. J. Physiol.* 124, 238.

WINDER, C. V., WINDER, H. O. and GESELL, R. (1933) *Am. J. Physiol.* 105, 311.

WINTERSTEIN, H. (1953) *Acta Physiol. Latinoam.* 3, 195. Cited by HEYMANS and NEIL, 1958.

WINTERSTEIN, H. (1956) *New Engl. J. Med.* 255, 216, 262, 331. Cited by HEYMANS and NEILL, 1958.

WINTERSTEIN, H. and GOKHAN, N. (1953a) *Arch. Exp. Path. Pharmak.* **219**, 192.

WINTERSTEIN, H. and GOKHAN, N. (1953b) *Arch. intern. pharmacodynamie* **93**, 2, 212.

WITZLER, E. (1953) *Arch. Ges. Physiol.* **257**, 244.

WITZLER, E., BARTELS, H., BUDDE, H. and MOCHIZUCKI, M. (1955) *Arch. Ges. Physiol.* **261**, 211.

WYSS, O. A. M. (1949) *Ann. Rev. Physiol.* **11**, 467.

YEL'TSINA, N. V. (1948) *Biochemistry* **4**, 351.

YEMEL'YANOVA, A. V. (1954) *Physiol. J. U.S.S.R.* **40**, 1, 59.

YUDAYEV, N. A. and PANKOV, YU. A. (1958) *Problems of Endocrinol. and Hormonotherapy* **2**, 35.

YUZBASHINSKAYA, P. KH. (1938) *Pharmacology* **1**, 2, 3, 66.

ZAKUSOV, V. V. (1933) *Physiol. J. U.S.S.R.* **16**, 4.

ZAKUSOV, V. V. (1935) *Scientific papers of the Kirov Military Medical Academy* **11**, 258.

ZAKUSOV, V. V. (1938) *Physiol. J. U.S.S.R.* **25**, 4, 569.

ZAKUSOV, V. V. (1939) *Pharmacol. and Toxicol.* **2** (2), 20.

ZBURZHINSKII, V. K. (1958) *Pharmacol. and Toxicol.* **21**, 4, 87.

ZBURZHINSKII, V. K. (1960) *Problems of work hygiene*, p. 58, Leningrad.

ZBURZHINSKII, V. K. (1961) *Pharmacol and Toxicol.* **24**, 2, 215.

ZUNZ, E. and TREMONTI, P. (1931) *Compt. rend. soc. biol.* **106**, 1239.